CONTENTS

Cover Picture: Queenwood Golf Lodge, Bowood (page 23)

Your guide to holiday relaxation.

Key to symbols

All prices shown include VAT

 MasterCard accepted

VISA Visa accepted

AMERICAN EXPRESS American Express accepted

(D) Diners Club accepted

Quiet location

Access for wheelchairs to at least one bedroom and public rooms

Children welcome, with minimum age where applicable

Dogs accommodated in rooms or kennels

At least one room has a four-poster bed

Satellite/cable TV in all bedrooms

Fax machine available in bedrooms

No-smoking rooms (at least 1 no-smoking bedroom)

Indoor swimming pool

Outdoor swimming pool

Tennis court on site

Croquet lawn on site

Fishing can be arranged

Golf course on site or nearby, with an arrangement allowing guests to play

Shooting can be arranged

Riding can be arranged

(H) Venue has a helicopter landing pad

How to use the Johansens Holiday Cottages Guide

Welcome to this first edition of Johansens Recommended Holiday Cottages. Each of the properties featured has been visited and approved by a member of our inspection team responsible for selecting recommendations for our guides to Hotels, Traditional Inns, Country Houses and Business Meeting Venues throughout the British Isles. The same unashamedly subjective quality standards have been adhered to in creating this selection of houses, cottages and apartments.

To find a property you can either turn to the map on page 4, search the indexes on pages 85 to 87 or look for the town or village where you wish to stay in the main body of the guide. Place names appear at the top of each page in alphabetical order.

Symbols used are explained on this page and other special facilities are described in the shaded panel beside each recommendation. Prices are per property per week inclusive of typical charges for electricity etc and usually vary according to the time of year from the lowest to highest rate shown. **Many of these recommendations offer shorter breaks as well. Please contact the properties direct to ask for prices.**

Johansens do not operate as a booking agent and readers should be aware that they are dealing directly with the owners when making a booking. We hope you enjoy our recommendations and that you will let us know of your experience either by letter or by using one of the guest survey forms at the back of this book.

Copies of other titles in the Johansens range may be ordered using the forms on pages 89 to 96 or by calling the order hotline on Freephone 0800 269397. The guides are also obtainable at most good bookshops.

Published by Johansens Limited, Therese House, Glasshouse Yard, London EC1A 4JN
Tel: 020 7566 9700 Fax: 020 7490 2538
Find Johansens on the Internet at: **www.johansens.com** E-mail: carol@johansens.com

Publishing Director:	Peter Hancock
P.A. to Publishing Director:	Carol Sweeney
Editorial Manager:	Yasmin Razak
Regional Inspectors:	Geraldine Bromley, Robert Bromley, Julie Dunkley, Pat Gillson, Martin Greaves, Joan Henderson, Marie Iversen, Pauline Mason, John O'Neill, Mary O'Neill, Fiona Patrick, Brian Sandell
Production Director:	Daniel Barnett
Production Controller:	Kevin Bradbrook
Senior Designer:	Michael Tompsett
Designer:	Sue Dixon
Webmaster:	John Lea
Copywriters:	Simon Duke, Norman Flack, Warren Knock
Sales and Marketing Manager:	Laurent Martinez
Marketing Executive:	Stephen Hoskin
Sales Administrator:	Susan Butterworth
P.A. to Managing Director :	Glenda Walshaw
Managing Director:	Andrew Warren

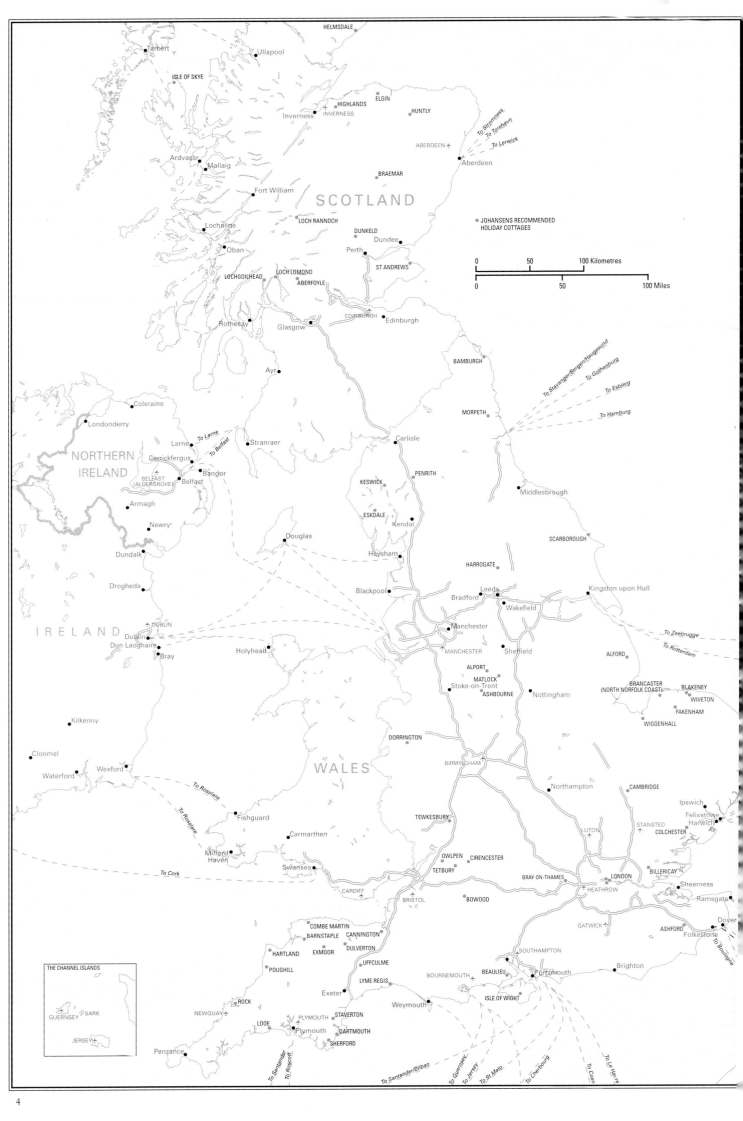

Tarbert

Ullapool

HELMSDALE

ISLE OF SKYE

HIGHLANDS
Inverness INVERNESS

ELGIN

HUNTLY

To Stromness
To Torshavn
To Lerwick

Ardvasar
Mallaig

ABERDEEN
Aberdeen

BRAEMAR

Fort William

SCOTLAND

Lochaline

LOCH RANNOCH

Oban

DUNKELD
Dundee

JOHANSENS RECOMMENDED
HOLIDAY COTTAGES

LOCHGOILHEAD

LOCH LOMOND
ABERFOYLE

Perth

ST ANDREWS

0   50   100 Kilometres

0   50   100 Miles

Rothesay

Glasgow

EDINBURGH
Edinburgh

Ayr

BAMBURGH

Coleraine

To Stavanger/Bergen/Haugesund
To Gothenburg
To Esbjerg

Londonderry

MORPETH

To Hamburg

Larne
To Larne
To Belfast

Stranraer

Carlisle

NORTHERN
IRELAND

Carrickfergus
Bangor

PENRITH

KESWICK

Middlesbrough

BELFAST
(ALDERGROVE)
Belfast

Armagh

ESKDALE
Kendal

Newry

SCARBOROUGH

Douglas

HARROGATE

Dundalk

Heysham

Drogheda

Blackpool

Leeds
Bradford

Kingston upon Hull

IRELAND

Wakefield

Manchester

To Zeebrugge

DUBLIN
Dublin
Dun Laoghaire
Bray

MANCHESTER

Sheffield

To Rotterdam

ALFORD

Holyhead

ALPORT
MATLOCK
Stoke-on-Trent
ASHBOURNE

Nottingham

BRANCASTER
(NORTH NORFOLK COAST)
BLAKENEY
WIVETON
FAKENHAM
WIGGENHALL

Kilkenny

DORRINGTON

Clonmel

WALES

BIRMINGHAM

CAMBRIDGE

Waterford
Wexford

To Rosslare

Northampton

Ipswich

To Rosslare

Fishguard

TEWKESBURY

Felixstowe
Harwich

STANSTED

LUTON

COLCHESTER

Carmarthen

OWLPEN
CIRENCESTER

Milford
Haven

Swansea

TETBURY

BILLERICAY

To Cork

CARDIFF

BRAY-ON-THAMES

LONDON

Sheerness

BOWOOD

HEATHROW

Ramsgate

BRISTOL

COMBE MARTIN
BARNSTAPLE
CANNINGTON

GATWICK

ASHFORD

Dover
Folkestone

HARTLAND
EXMOOR

DULVERTON

To Boulogne

POUGHILL

UFFCULME

SOUTHAMPTON

BEAULIEU

Brighton

LYME REGIS

BOURNEMOUTH

Portsmouth

THE CHANNEL ISLANDS

Exeter

Weymouth

ISLE OF WIGHT

ROCK

NEWQUAY

PLYMOUTH
STAVERTON

GUERNSEY
SARK

LOOE
Plymouth
DARTMOUTH
SHERFORD

JERSEY

Penzance

To Santander
To Roscoff

To Santander/Bilbao

To Guernsey
To Jersey
To St Malo

To Cherbourg

To Le Havre

To Caen

4

TASTER'S CHOICE

Robin Davis

HILDON FROM

Britain Bubbles to Top

The fast-approaching holidays mean parties, and while Champagne is festive, a non-alcoholic choice for guests is a must. With its tiny bubbles, sparkling water makes a good substitute, but it can difficult to choose among the many brands.

Today's panel tasted 10 sparkling waters — seven imported from Europe and three domestic brands — but only one American-bottled water scored high enough to rate.

The panel found dramatic differences in taste. Several waters scored high and close together, then scores dropped off for the remaining products. Panelists said they could taste differences in the mineral content; the amount of carbonation also played a role in what they liked.

The top scorer was Great Britain's **Hildon** (750 milliters, $2.49 at Draeger's). One panelist thought it was "clean and pure-tasting;" two enjoyed its carbonation. All would buy it.

Vals (16.9 ounces, $1.69 at Draeger's) from France scored only one point lower. One panelist commented on its character, and three liked its strong mineral flavor. All would buy it.

California's **Calistoga** (one liter, 89-99 cents at many supermarkets) came in third. One panelist described it as "exciting." Two noted a salty taste. Four

would buy it; one might buy it.

Another British water, **Ty Nant** (750 milliliters, $2.19 at Andronico's) was only two points below Calistoga. One panelist thought the carbonation tasted fake, but another liked the "tingly" bubbles. Three would buy it, one might, and one would not.

The most expensive brand, **Acqua della Madonna** (750 milliliters, $3.19, at Draeger's) from Italy, came in fifth. One panelist thought the salty mineral taste "lingers unpleasantly," but another described it as "snappy." One would buy it, two might, and two would not.

Panelists were divided on **Perrier** (750 milliliters, $1.29 at many supermarkets) from France. One liked the salty, mineral flavor, and another liked the tiny bubbles. But two others thought it was nondescript. Two would buy it; three would not.

Apollinaris (from Germany), Crystal Geyser (from the U.S.), San Pellegrino (from Italy) and Arrowhead (from the U.S.) scored too low to rate.

Correction: The store listed as a source for Jolt and Virgin colas in the October 16 Taster's Choice column was incorrect. The colas can be purchased at Draeger's on the Peninsula.

Robin Davis is a Chronicle staff critic.

SPARKLING WATER

TASTERS	Hildon	Vals	Calistoga	Ty Nant	Acqua della Madonna	Perrier
Bowe	18	16	9	16	11	9
Carroll	16	16	16	18	10	16
Katzl	16	16	17	13	17	7
Passot	16	16	17	16	12	17
Webber	12	13	12	6	6	6
TOTALS	78	77	71	69	56	55

Panelists were Dan Bowe, associate culinary director, Center for Culinary Development; John P. Carroll, cookbook author; Donna Katzl, chef-owner Cafe For All Seasons, San Francisco; Roland Passot, chef-owner, La Folie in San Francisco and Left Bank in Larkspur and Menlo Park; and Kirk Webber, chef-owner, Cafe Kati, San Francisco. All products are tasted blind. A perfect score for any product would be 100.

and a deep burgundy, color sc — but some of the service st parted when Serrano left. nately, like a well-oiled ma the new people fit into the se cadence of service. The wa there when you need them, never hover. There's a p

About Johansens

Established in 1982, Johansens is a publishing company owned by the Daily Mail & General Trust Plc. It is not a consortium or agency so there are no booking fees or commission charged to either the user of the guide or the owner of a recommended property.

Annual visits by a team of 12 regional inspectors ensure that Johansens' unashamedly subjective quality standards are maintained. Over half of the properties inspected each year fail to achieve Johansens Recommendation and therefore do not appear in our guides.

For those who require help in finding the right venue for a luxury break, business meeting or an interesting place to visit please refer to the full range of Johansens titles depicted on the outside back cover. These include guides to recommended hotels in Europe, North America and Southern Africa.

All Johansens recommendations, including those found within this title, are represented in full colour on our website which can be viewed at www.johansens.com
The site offers searching by location, facilities, price or 'key word' and displays availability of accommodation at many hotels, inns and houses on given dates.

"FOR BEST BEFORE DATE SEE CAP"
Bottled at source, Broughton, Hampshire
750mle
WELL... DE GUSTIBUS NON EST DISPUTANDUM
HILDON
AN ENGLISH
NATURAL MINERAL WATER
OF EXCEPTIONAL TASTE
DELIGHTFULLY STILL
Composition in accordance with the results of the officially recognized analysis 26 March 1992
Hildon Ltd., Broughton, Hampshire SO20 8DG, ☎ 01794-301 747
Hildon Ltd., Broughton, Hampshire SO20 8DG, ☎ 01794 - 301 747
STUDIO BRUSIUS

London

London recommendations represent a fine selection of fully-serviced, luxury apartments. Our choice is based on location, reputation, value for money and excellence, above all else. The Johansens guest can be comfortably accommodated within easy reach of the principal shopping areas, museums, galleries, restaurants, theatres and Wimbledon!

The Millennium Dome

What's new in the capital?

• The Millennium Dome is located beside the Thames on Greenwich peninsula. It is almost finished and opens on 1st January 2000.

• Take a look at the Millennium Countdown Clock at the Old Royal Observatory and take a glimpse of the Dome itself.

• The Millennium Bridge is currently being built across the Thames near St Paul's Cathedral along with the Millennium Wheel which will offer visitors an amazing 30-mile view over London. This should be completed by the autumn.

• The British Film Institute opened a 482 seat cinema on the South Bank on 1st May. The £20 million cinema boasts the UK's biggest cinema screen: 20 metres high by 26 metres wide with an IMAX projection system and digital surround sound. The cinema will be open seven days a week and tickets cost £6.50 for adults and £4.50 for children.

• London Zoo has created a £4.4 million conservation education centre promoting conservation in the natural world and endeavours to change our approach to zoos in the 21st century. Built in a new glass pavilion, the Web of Life Exhibition brings people closer to live animals in amazing settings.

• The FA Premier League Hall of Fame has been created in the old County Hall. This attraction offers visitors the chance to experience an entertaining and informative celebration of English football from past to present incorporating wax models and a wall of hand casts.

• Madame Tussaud's Rock Circus has now completed it's multi-million pound redevelopment and offers visitors a range of audiovisual and animatronic effects and wax portraits of some of the biggest stars in music.

For further information contact:

London Tourist Board
Glen House
Stag Place
London
SW1E 5LT

Tel: 0207 932 2000
Fax: 0207 932 0222
Website: www.LondonTown.com

9

PRICES

Smallest Apartment

from £178
per night
from £1122
per week

Largest Apartment

from £437
per night
from £2781
per week

OTHER FACILITIES

Cot available

Shop nearby

Parking facilities

Laundry Service

Prepared meals available

Maid Service

Garden furniture

Bicycle Hire

DRAYCOTT HOUSE APARTMENTS

10 DRAYCOTT AVENUE, CHELSEA, LONDON SW3 3AA
TEL: 020 7584 4659 FAX: 020 7225 3694 E-MAIL: sales@draycotthouse.co.uk
OWNERS:

Positioned in the heart of Chelsea on a charming tree-lined avenue, Draycott Apartments offer visitors an extremely friendly and homely base to discover London. Housed in an attractive period building, the apartments have been individually designed to the very highest standard. Marrying the convenience, comfort and seclusion, the apartments provide ideal surroundings for both business and leisure visitors. With a choice of one, two or three bedrooms, these wonderfully appointed apartments are spacious and well-maintained. Some have private balconies, overlooking the quaint courtyard and a roof terrace. Each apartment is equipped with all the home comforts imaginable, including cable television, video, stereo and private lines for telephone, fax or the Internet. Upon arrival, visitors are given complementary provisions and milk and newspapers are delivered daily,

with a maid service from Monday to Friday. Draycott House also offers covered garage parking and an in-house laundry room. Laundry and dry cleaning can also be arranged. Visitors can make use of an introduction to an exclusive West End health club, while Draycott can provide cars, catering, travel and theatre arrangements or child-minders upon request. London's swinging West End, with its plethora of bars, restaurants and theatres is in easy walking distance. In the immediate vicinity are the Natural History Museum, Brompton Cross and Knightsbridge. A shopper's paradise, Draycott House is minutes away from Sloane Square and the King's Road. **Directions:** Draycott House is located on the corner of Draycott Road Avenue and Draycott Place. The nearest tube station is Sloane Square. The apartments are available for as little as one night.

Apartment Name	Sleeps	Bedrooms	Shower	Bath
ONE BEDROOMED	2	1	1	1
TWO BEDROOMED	3/4	2	1	1
THREE BEDROOMED	5/6	3	1	1

PRICES

Smallest Apartment

from £1175 plus VAT per week

Largest Apartment

from £1475 plus VAT per week

OTHER FACILITIES

Cot available

Shop nearby

Laundry Service

Parking facilities

Maid Service

Garden furniture

THE LEXHAM APARTMENTS

32-38 LEXHAM GARDENS, KENSINGTON, LONDON W8 5JE
TEL: 020 7559 4444 FAX: 020 7559 4400 E-MAIL: reservations@lexham.com

The Lexham stands tall and graciously in a quiet, tree-lined garden square in the heart of one of the most exclusive areas of London. It has been created from two of the early, elegant Victorian buildings that are the hallmark of this oasis of tranquillity and has a spacious and delightful landscaped garden at the rear where guests can relax on warm days and evenings. Close by are the fashionable and exclusive shops and restaurants of Kensington, Knightsbridge and Chelsea. Within easy reach are the West End theatres and some of the capital's major tourist attractions. All 31 one and two bedroom luxury apartments combine comfort, flexibility, privacy and security. They are tastefully decorated and stylishly furnished to provide convenient and ideal surroundings for a family or business visit. Each is spacious, light and airy and is equipped with all home-from-home comforts, including cable television, safe, voice mail and private telephone and fax lines. Kitchens are full-sized and extremely well appointed with accessories ranging from a dishwasher to a washing machine and tumble dryer. Many of the apartments feature extra comforts such as a sofa bed. Additional beds and cots can also be provided at no extra charge. There is a daily maid service on weekdays, 24 hour porterage and reservations for a restaurant, theatre, car, cycle or nearby health club with swimming pool can be arranged. A laundry service is available and outside catering can be supplied should guests want to entertain or have a break from the kitchen. Minimum stay at the Lexham is seven days. **Directions:** The nearest underground stations are Gloucester Road and High Street Kensington.

Apartment Name	Sleeps	Bedrooms	Shower	Bath
ONE BEDROOM	2/4	1	1	1
TWO BEDROOM	4/6	2	1	1

THE PRESTON SUITE

2 ORCHID COURT, 130 PRESTON ROAD, WEMBLEY, MIDDLESEX
TEL: 07071 885555 FAX: 01276 31856 E-MAIL: votel.co.uk
OWNERS: Votel

Designed to the very highest standard, the Preston Suite is a privately-owned one bedroom ground floor apartment that would appeal to both corporate long-term visitors and private travellers. An ideal base from which to explore London, the Preston Suite has everything one would expect in a luxury apartment. The beautifully appointed kitchen has every modern convenience, including a microwave oven, washer/dryer, dishwasher, bone china and crystal glasses. The spacious sitting room has a stereo, extensive CD and video library, cable TV and video, as well as a selection of books and games. A sofa bed and a reclining massage chair also adorn the sitting room. Extra touches include daily newspapers, fresh flowers and fruit weekly and a mobile phone for the duration of each stay. For the business visitor there is also a computer, modem point, fax/copier and colour printer.

Visitors can also take advantage of the bright patio that leads to the landscaped garden, overlooked by the luxurious bedroom. The Preston Suite is situated in a block of 22 modern apartments and benefits from a 24 hour helpline as well as a video entry system. Nearby Barn Hill provides glorious walks and stunning views of London. Hatfield House, St. Albans and Whipsnade Zoo are all easily reached. Those with a passion for fashion must visit Brent Cross, a large shopping centre within the vicinity. Long term guests are given a complimentary champagne hamper on arrival. **Directions:** The Preston Suite is just 15 minutes from A40/M40, and a similar distance from M1. It is just off A406 North Circular Road. Equidistant from Preston Road and Wembley tube stations, access is easy to central London, via the Metropolitan and Bakerloo lines.

Apartment Name	Sleeps	Bedrooms	Shower	Bath
THE PRESTON SUITE	2/4	1		1

England

England has so much to offer – castles, cathedrals, museums and the opportunity to stay in areas of great historical importance.

Castle Combe, Wiltshire

Regional Tourist Boards

Cumbria Tourist Board
Ashleigh, Holly Road, Windermere
Cumbria LA23 2AQ
Tel: 015394 44444
England's most beautiful lakes and tallest mountains reach out from the Lake District National Park to a landscape of spectacular coasts, hills and dales.

East of England Tourist Board
Toppesfield Hall, Hadleigh
Suffolk IP7 5DN
Tel: 01473 822922
Cambridgeshire, Essex, Hertfordshire, Bedfordshire, Norfolk, Suffolk and Lincolnshire.

Heart of England Tourist Board
Woodside, Larkhill Road.
Worcester WR5 2EZ
Tel: 01905 763436
Gloucestershire, Hereford & Worcester, Shropshire, Staffordshire, Warwickshire, West Midlands, Derbyshire, Leicestershire, Northamptonshire, Nottinghamshire & Rutland. Represents the districts of Cherwell & West Oxfordshire in the county of Oxfordshire.

London Tourist Board
Glen House, Stag Place
London SW1E 5LT
Tel: 0171 932 2000

Northumbria Tourist Board
Aykley Heads
Durham DH1 5UX
Tel: 0191 375 3000
The Tees Valley, Durham, Northumberland, Tyne & Wear.

North West Tourist Board
Swan House, Swan Meadow Road, Wigan Pier
Lancashire WN3 5BB
Tel: 01942 821222
Cheshire, Greater Manchester, Lancashire, Merseyside & the High Peak District of Derbyshire.

South East England Tourist Board
The Old Brew House, Warwick Park, Tunbridge
Wells, Kent TN2 5TU
Tel: 01892 540766
East & West Sussex, Kent & Surrey

Southern Tourist Board
40 Chamberlayne Road, Eastleigh
Hampshire SO50 5JH
Tel: 01703 620006
East & North Dorset, Hampshire, Isle of Wight, Berkshire, Buckinghamshire & Oxfordshire.

West Country Tourist Board
60 St David's Hill, Exeter
Devon EX4 4SY
Tel: 01392 425426
Bath & NE Somerset, Bristol, Cornwall and the Isles of Scilly, Devon, Dorset (Western), North Somerset & Wiltshire.

Yorkshire Tourist Board
312 Tadcaster Road
York YO2 2HF
Tel: 01904 707961
Yorkshire and North & North East Lincolnshire.

Further Information

English Heritage
23rd Floor, Portland HouseStag Place
London SW1E 5EE
Tel: 0171-973 3000
Offers an unrivalled choice of properties to visit.

Historic Houses Association
2 Chester Street
London SW1X 7BB
Tel: 0171-259 5688
Ensures the survival of historic houses and gardens in private ownership in Great Britain

The National Trust
36 Queen Anne's Gate
London SW1H 9AS
Tel: 0171-222 9251
Cares for more than 590,000 acres of countryside and over 400 historic buildings.

PRICES

Cottage
from £200
to £290
per week

OTHER FACILITIES

Scenic views

Cot available

Shop nearby

Parking facilities

Garden furniture

Barbecue

WOODTHORPE HALL COUNTRY COTTAGES

WOODTHORPE, NR ALFORD, LINCOLNSHIRE LN13 0DD
TEL: 01507 450294
OWNER: Mrs J Stubbs

Cowslip Cottage is situated in a quiet rural location enjoying 500 acres of rolling countryside on the edge of the beautiful Lincolnshire Wolds yet only a couple of miles from the sandy beach at Mablethorpe. Sleeping five people, the cottage is light and airy with attractive and comfortable furnishings and fully-equipped with all the necessities needed to create a home-away-from-home environment. The cottage has its own parking space and a patio with a table, chairs and a barbecue. There are other cottages on the estate which have not been inspected by Johansens. The calm, relaxing ambience belies the fact that there is plenty to do on the cottage's doorstep. There is an 18-hole golf course suitable for both novices and enthusiasts and a large fishing lake, well-stocked with carp, perch and orfe, on site. An award-winning garden centre and an aquatic centre all form part of the estate. The restaurant and bar, located at the Golf Club, is an ideal venue for enjoying a leisurely drink or taking a break from the kitchen and enjoying a fine selection of dishes. There is a tarmacked landing strip for guests wishing to arrive by air. Day excursions include perusing the market towns of the Wolds, exploring the historic city of Lincoln or, for the more adventurous, motor racing at Cadwell Park. The towns of Louth, Alford and Mablethorpe are also worth a visit. Please note, prices exclude metered electricity. **Directions:** From the A1 take the A16 at Stamford to Alford. Woodthorpe Hall is situated three miles beyond on the B1373.

Cottage Name	Sleeps	Bedrooms	Shower	Bath
COWSLIP	5	3	1	1

THE CHAPEL

HARTHILL HALL, ALPORT, NR BAKEWELL, DERBYSHIRE DE45 1LH
TEL: 01629 636190 FAX: 01629 636967 E-MAIL: nicola@harthillhall.co.uk
OWNERS: Nicola and Peter Bunting

This dramatic historic hall stands in 14 acres of the Peak District National Park just three miles from Bakewell, a valley market town with many fine 17th and 18th centuries buildings surrounded by richly wooded hills stretching to high moorland. A cluster of listed buildings dating from the Domesday Book have been delightfully converted into cottages offering excellent accommodation for those seeking to explore the delights of Derbyshire. They surround a medieval cobbled courtyard and retain a wealth of original features, including thick stone diving walls, massive oak beams, mullion windows and flagstone floors. The Chapel, dating from 1296 and originally the Hall House, ceased to be a place of worship in 1545. Owners Nicola and Peter Bunting are dealers of early English furniture and antiques and this is reflected throughout.

There are other cottages on the estate which have not been inspected by Johansens. Medieval stonework and a flagstone entrance floor welcome guests into the interior. There is an enchanting dining room, an elegant sitting room with gas fired Victorian barrel stove and a fully fitted kitchen opening onto a south facing terrace and views over open countryside. A superb oak four-poster is featured in one of the three upstairs bedrooms, a gleaming Victorian brass bed is in another. Guests can enjoy a heated indoor pool, sauna, Jacuzzi, solarium and mini-gym, spend time rambling, walking or visiting numerous stately homes and National Trust properties in the area. **Directions:** Take A6 north of Rowsley or south from Bakewell. Turn onto B5056 towards Winster and Harthill Hall is on the right after approximately 1½ miles.

Cottage Name	Sleeps	Bedrooms	Shower	Bath
THE CHAPEL	6	3		2

OTHER FACILITIES

Scenic views

Cot available

Shop nearby

Parking facilities

Open Fire

Laundry Service

Garden furniture

Barbecue

Bicycle Hire

SLADE HOUSE FARM

ILAM, ASHBOURNE, DERBYSHIRE DE6 2BB
TEL: 01538 308 123 FAX: 01538 308 777
OWNERS: Alan and Pat Philp

With exceptional views of the idyllic Staffordshire countryside and bracing walks from its doorstep, Slade House Farm is a delightful retreat on the edge of the Peak National Park. Ideal for unwinding, the three cottages on this lovingly maintained seven-acre farm each has its own picturesque garden and offers utter privacy and seclusion. Slade House, the largest of the three, is a former yeoman's abode dating back to the 1640s. With exposed beams and antique furniture throughout, as well as a log fire in both kitchen and living room, it exudes a rural homeliness that complements its magnificent views of the National Park. Slade Cottage, a carefully converted wing of the farmhouse, has its own courtyard and cobbled patio which again command breathtaking views of the countryside. With quarry tiled floors, it still retains the original farmhouse range. The smallest of the three, Slade Tops, was converted from a barn and sleeps two people in homely surroundings. The sitting room, boasting a pine ceiling, gives onto the airy kitchen and dining area. All the properties are totally non-smoking. The range of activities in the area is also impressive. Nearby Alton Towers, whose bustle is in stark contrast to the silence of the Slade House farm, is perfect for a raucous family day out. The Roaches, also in the immediate vicinity, is famed throughout the land for its rock climbing. Cycling is perhaps the best way to explore the local cycle trails. Short breaks available. Free colour brochure on request. **Directions:** From Ashbourne, take the A523 towards Leek. Continue approximately two miles beyond the A52 turning on the left, and follow the signs on the right to Calton and then to Ilam.

Cottage Name	Sleeps	Bedrooms	Shower	Bath
SLADE HOUSE	8	4	2	3
SLADE COTTAGE	4	2	1	1
SLADE TOPS	2	1	1	1

PRICES

Smallest Cottage
£500
per week

Largest Cottage
£900
per week

OTHER FACILITIES

Scenic views

Cot available

Parking facilities

Laundry Service

Maid Service

EASTWELL MEWS

EASTWELL PARK, BOUGHTON LEES, NR ASHFORD, KENT TN25 4HR
TEL: 01233 213000 FAX: 01233 635530
OWNERS: Eastwell Manor Ltd

Eastwell Mews is a new, prestigious and tasteful conversion of a Victorian stable block of historic Eastwell Manor, situated in 62 acres of lovely grounds in the midst of a 3,000 acre estate in the peaceful 'Garden of England'. The Manor, now a luxury hotel, was once the home of Queen Victoria's second son, Prince Albert, and his wife. The Mews consist of 19 courtyard country cottages of one to three bedrooms which are peaceful holiday or weekend retreats for couples and families wishing to get away from it all. Each appealing cottage is delightfully and individually furnished and decorated and either has views over the Manor gardens, the Kent countryside or the tranquil courtyards. Some have patio doors leading out to their own garden. Guests want for nothing in the cottages. Each is completely self-contained and has full central heating,

direct dial telephone, fax and voice mail facilities, en suite bedrooms, lounge and dining areas and a fully equipped kitchen There is satellite television in the bedrooms and lounge where there is also a video recorder. Maid service and baby sitting are available. All of the facilities at Eastwell Manor are available to cottage guests. These include its award winning restaurant, bars, gymnasium, all-weather tennis courts, indoor and outdoor heated pools and spa pool. Eastwell Mews is an ideal base for visiting historic Canterbury, Leeds Castle, Dover and a number of charming market towns. It is also situated near to the Ashford stop for the Eurostar rail journey to France. **Directions:** From the M20, exit at junction 9. Take the A28 towards Canterbury and then the A251 signed Faversham. Boughton Lees is three miles north of Ashford.

Cottage Name	Sleeps	Bedrooms	Shower	Bath
TYPE A	2	1	1	1
TYPE B	3	2	1	1
TYPE C	4	2	1	1
TYPE D	5	3	1	1
TYPE E	6	3	1	1

OUTCHESTER MANOR COTTAGES

OUTCHESTER, BELFORD, NORTHUMBERLAND NE70 7EB
TEL: 01668 213336 FAX: 01668 213174
OWNERS: Mr and Mrs J B Sutherland

This corner of Northumberland is comparatively empty, but what it lacks in large villages it makes up for in beauty. It has a superb coastline of rocky cliffs and sand dunes and a wonderful grey seal and seabird sanctuary on the bare volcanic rocks of the Farne Islands. There is a certain haunting quality which echoes the troubled and lawless past when English and Scottish armies went to war and local lords fought each other constantly until the late 16th century. Outchester Manor Cottages lie in a designated area of outstanding natural beauty between Belford village and the sea, close to the 8,000 acres Lindisfarne Natural Nature Reserve. The Farne Islands, retreat of Cuthbert, Bishop of Lindisfarne and a saint who helped develop the region as one of the first Christian kingdoms in England, can be visited by boat from Seahouses. Holy Island, with dramatic priory ruins and a castle, is reached at low tide by a causeway. The cottages surround an attractive courtyard and were rebuilt and refurbished in 1999. They are spacious, comfortable, well equipped and furnished to the highest standard. Each has a sitting room/kitchen with French doors opening onto a patio and lawned garden, central heating and a fully fitted kitchen that includes automatic washing machine and tumble drier. As well as long sandy beaches and moorland walks there are countless places to visit. Castles at Bamburgh, Dunstanburgh and Alnwick, Elizabethan fortifications at Berwick upon Tweed and, to the west, the grandeur of the Cheviot Hills. **Directions:** From A1 north turn right onto B1342 towards Bamburgh. A mile after crossing the railway the cottages are on the left.

Cottage Name	Sleeps	Bedrooms	Shower	Bath
OYSTERSHELL COTTAGE	6	3	1	1
CURLEW COTTAGE	4	2	1	1
KITTIWAKE COTTAGE	4	2	1	1
PUFFIN COTTAGE	2	1	1	1

PRICES

Smallest Cottage
from £450
to £800
per week

Largest Cottage
from £600
to £1200
per week

OTHER FACILITIES

Scenic views

Cot available

Shop nearby

Parking facilities

Garden furniture

Barbecue

Bicycle Hire

CORFFE

TAWSTOCK, BARNSTAPLE, DEVON EX31 3HZ
TEL/FAX: 01271 342588
OWNERS: Christopher and Edwina Wheeler-Grix and Peter Bath

Corffe is an imposing 18th century, three storey high mansion with stuccoed front and deep bracketed eaves rising high over the pretty village of Tawstock and commanding panoramic views over beautiful countryside and the wooded valley of the River Taw. Until 1978 it was owned by a titled family and is mentioned in The Buildings of England (Devon) by Nikolaus Pevsner. Its outbuildings have now been converted into attractive and comfortable holiday cottages which share 3½ acres of grounds and woodlands and an excellent range of facilities. The largest, Hillside, sleeps eight, has three bedrooms, two bathrooms and a beamed ceiling. Two storey Corner sleeps four in two ground floor bedrooms. The spacious living room and kitchen are upstairs. Each cottage is delightfully furnished and has every modern facility, including full-size cooker, a microwave oven, refrigerator/freezer, radiant fires, satellite television, patio access and many other amenities. A laundry room with coin-operated automatic washing machines and tumble dryers is nearby. There are other cottages on the estate which have not been inspected by Johansens. Corffe offers total peace and seclusion with the grounds providing tranquil walks and a special beauty whatever the season. Leisure facilities include an all-weather tennis court, a wonderful award winning heated indoor pool with lawned sun terrace, a children's paddling pool and a relaxing Jacuzzi. The 18-hole Portmore Golf Club, riding and fishing are nearby. **Directions:** Exit M5 at junction 27. Join A361 towards Barnstaple and then A39 towards Bideford. At Roundwell roundabout exit for Torrington. Travel through Eastacombe and on entering Tawstock, Corffe is on the right.

Cottage Name	Sleeps	Bedrooms	Shower	Bath
HILLSIDE COTTAGE	8	3	2	2
16TH C CORNER COTTAGE	4	2	1	1

A member of
Premier Cottages Direct

PRICES

Cottage
from £459
to £859
per week

OTHER FACILITIES

Scenic views

Cot available

Parking facilities

Open Fire

Maid Service

Garden furniture

Barbecue

CULVERLEY OLD FARM COTTAGE

CULVERLEY OLD FARM HOUSE, BEAULIEU, HAMPSHIRE SO42 7YP
TEL/FAX: 01590 612260 E-MAIL: v.m.heathcote-hacker@culverley.screaming.net
OWNERS: Mrs Vivien Heathcote Hacker

Winner of the Southern Tourist Board's "England for Excellence Self-Catering Holiday of the Year Award", Culverley Old Farm Cottage combines unadulterated luxury with complete seclusion. Surrounded by a beautiful garden and five acres of rolling lawns and paddocks, the nearest neighbour, other than the main house, is three fields away. The cottage has a simply idyllic garden where roses, honeysuckle and clematis abound. A veritable sun-trap, it is perfect for family barbecues. The interior is magnificently appointed and retains many of the original features, including stripped pitch pine doors in every room. The sitting room is spacious and airy and is dominated by a large open log fire. The master bedroom, otherwise known as the Honeymoon Suite, epitomises romance. The four-poster bed is flanked by deep-pile sheepskin rugs, while the room is literally swamped by antique polished pine furniture. The kitchen, painted in a soothing terracotta colour, is also a delight. Containing a long refectory antique table, it is ideal for languorous lunches or romantic dinners. Two miles away are the world famous National Motor Museum and the Cistercian Abbey ruins. In nearby Bucklers Hard, where Nelson built his ships, the Maritime Museum gives a fascinating insight into England's sea-faring history. There is a golf course in nearby Dibden while horse-back tours of the New Forest can also be arranged. Please contact the owner by telephone, fax or e-mail for directions.

Cottage Name	Sleeps	Bedrooms	Shower	Bath
OLD FARM COTTAGE	6	3	2	2

Apartment
from £350
to £800
per week

THE PUMP HOUSE APARTMENT

132 CHURCH STREET, GREAT BURSTEAD, ESSEX CM11 2TR
TEL: 01277 656579 FAX: 01277 631160
OWNERS: Edwina and John Bayliss

Situated in some of the most picturesque countryside in rural South East England, the Pump House Apartment is an immaculately maintained self-contained two-storey apartment in the country village of Great Burstead. Spacious and fully-equipped, it is an extremely comfortable home away from home. Part of a modern house of interesting character, Pump House is set in its own secluded gardens, with an oriental pond and paddocks. Visitors can avail of an outdoor swimming pool heated to 80 degrees from May to September. Pump House is very flexible and the Apartment can be let as a one, two or three bedroomed residence. In each case two beautifully appointed lounges are available, in addition to an elegant dining room and an excellently designed first floor kitchen with views over the pretty gardens below. The Pump House is the perfect place to discover the treasures of south east England. The village of Great Burstead is simply steeped in history. Its 14th century church has links with one of the Pilgrim Fathers and early settlers of the USA. Visitors to Pump House can reach London, Cambridge, Canterbury, Colchester and the Constable Country in under an hour's drive. Walks in the nearby countryside are a pleasure, while golf, tennis and badminton are among the many sports available in the vicinity. **Directions:** Leave the M25 at junction 29 and join the A127. Travel in the direction of Southend and then turn onto the A176 (Noak Hill Road) travelling towards Billericay. Church Street is on the right, with Pump House on the left before the church.

Apartment Name	Sleeps	Bedrooms	Shower	Bath
PUMP HOUSE APARTMENT	2/6	1/3	1	2

COUNTRYSIDE COTTAGES

BECK FARM BARN, BECK FARM, SUSTEAD, NORFOLK NR11 8RY
TEL: 01263 768355/07041 564005/07979 231289

Blakeney is a picturesque fishing village on the north Norfolk coast perfect for artists, ramblers, sailors, birdwatchers or those just wanting to relax in comfort. There are three privately owned cottages available, two of which are situated close to the quayside. Built of the traditional local materials, brick and flint, Snuggler's Den and Tiller's Adrift are both attractively furnished and equipped to a high standard, the former providing a cosy holiday base for a couple, while the latter accommodates up to four people. Valentine Cottage, also of brick and flint is a few miles inland in the delightful small village of Great Snoring. Suitable for three adults, this cottage features exposed beams and beechwood floors, as well as a four-poster bed. The owners' attention to detail in the provision of equipment, the quality of maintenance and in touches such as welcoming flowers, hampers, sherry and a bottle of wine is evident in all three cottages. The personal service is attentive, yet unobtrusive and there is an on-call service for advice and help. English Tourist Board Highly Commended. Excellent tourist information and restaurant and pub recommendations are available. This coast is justly renowned for its splendid beaches and is equally noted for its profusion of bird life. The area has much to offer, from stately homes like Sandringham, Blickling and Holkham Hall to National Hunt Racing at Fakenham. Holt and Burnham Market are lively villages with good restaurants, while the active sportsman will enjoy the choice of several golf courses or the facilities for sailing nearby. **Directions:** Blakeney is some 10 miles from Cromer on A149 to Hunstanton. Great Snoring lies off B1388 from Blakeney to Fakenham.

Cottage Name	Sleeps	Bedrooms	Shower	Bath
SNUGGLERS DEN	2	1	1	
TILLER'S ADRIFT	4	2	1	1
VALENTINE COTTAGE	3	2	1	1

OTHER FACILITIES

Scenic views

Shop nearby

Parking facilities

Open Fire

Laundry Service

Prepared meals available

Maid Service

Garden furniture

Barbecue

QUEENWOOD GOLF LODGE

BOWOOD GOLF AND COUNTRY CLUB, DERRY HILL, CALNE, WILTSHIRE SN11 9PQ
TEL: 01249 822228 FAX: 01249 822218 E-MAIL: enquiries@bowood–estate.co.uk
OWNER: The Marquis of Lansdowne

This golfing enthusiast's paradise is a real gem! A luxurious Georgian manor house standing between the seventh and eighth fairways of one of the best 18-hole championship courses in the South of England with unlimited golf during guests' stay. Solid and attractive with lead-paned windows and tall, pattered chimneys it offers fabulous unspoilt views over the fairways, greens and countryside. Queenwood has every comfort and homely atmosphere of a private house, having been furnished to the highest standard by Lady Lansdowne, wife of the proprieter, The Marquis of Lansdowne, who owns Bowood House. Rented on an exclusive basis, the Lodge sleeps up to eight in four individually decorated twin rooms which are all en suite. There is a gorgeous, comfortable sitting room in which to relax before an open fire, a richly decorated dining room where another open fire gently warms guests during the winter months, and a study where quiet moments can be savoured. After a day of unlimited golf on the Bowood course visitors return to enjoy a dinner prepared and served by the Lodge Manager and staff. All menu requirements and wines are pre-selected so that you can simply sit back, relax and be pampered by candlelight. Breakfast is also prepared and served. Should golf not be your forte you may care to explore 18th century Bowood House and its enchanting gardens and grounds designed by 'Capability Brown', or stroll around the old market town of Calne, the picturesque village of Lacock or take in the delights of Bath. The lodge is not suitable for toddlers. Prices include breakfast, dinner and golf. **Directions:** From M4, exit at junction 17 and take A350 to Chippenham. From there join A4 towards Calne. Bowood is on your right.

Cottage Name	Sleeps	Bedrooms	Shower	Bath
QUEENWOOD GOLF LODGE	8	4	4	4

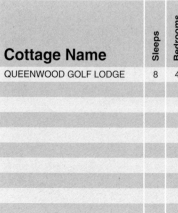

OTHER FACILITIES

Cot available

Parking facilities

Laundry Service

Prepared meals available

Maid Service

Garden furniture

Barbecue

DOWER HOUSE

AT CHAUNTRY HOUSE, 1 HIGH STREET, BRAY, BERKSHIRE SL6 2AB
TEL: 01628 673991 FAX: 01628 773089 E-MAIL: res@chauntryhouse.com
OWNERS: Luis Carvahlo and Alan Moxon

The Dower House is a detached cottage set in a private corner of the grounds of a small exclusive hotel, The Chauntry House in Bray. Its location between the cricket club and St. Michael's church in the historic village of Bray-on-Thames exudes the character and charm of rural England. The accommodation, which sleeps seven, includes a kitchen, dining room, hall, large sitting room and downstairs bathroom. The bedrooms comprise two doubles, one twin and one single, all of which feature en suite baths or showers. There is a gas effect fire in the sitting room and upstairs bathroom whilst all rooms have cable television and are centrally heated. The private patio overlooks the attractive gardens of The Chauntry House. Guests are welcome to use the hotel restaurant, subject to availability, as well as the full laundry and maid services which are available upon request. The Dower House is conveniently located for Heathrow airport and is near the Thames Valley business centres of Bracknell, Maidenhead and Slough. Places of interest in the vicinity include Ascot, Henley, Marlow and Windsor whilst central London is a mere 30 minutes away by train. **Directions:** From the M4, exit at junction 8/9 and take the A308M towards Windsor. Join B3028 turning left into Bray village just before the M4 overhead bridge. Continue into the village where the road turns sharply left. The entrance to Dower House is on the right, accessed through the Chauntry House entrance.

Cottage Name	Sleeps	Bedrooms	Shower	Bath
DOWER HOUSE	7	4	1	3
AT CHAUNTRY HOUSE				

PRICES

Smallest Cottage

from £250
to £439
per week

Largest Cottage

from £350
to £724
per week

OTHER FACILITIES

Scenic views

Cot available

Shop nearby

Parking facilities

Open Fire

Laundry Service

Prepared meals available

Garden furniture

Barbecue

Children's Play Area

WHITENSMERE FARM COTTAGES

ASHDON, SAFFRON WALDEN, ESSEX CB10 2JQ
TEL/FAX: 01799 584244 E-MAIL: gford@lineone.net
OWNER: Sue Ford

Set on an elevated plane with relaxing views of the lilting Cambridgeshire countryside, Whitensmere Farm provides every creature comfort for the complete home away from home. A tastefully renovated cluster of 18th century farm buildings, Whitensmere is surrounded by a restful and fragrant landscaped garden ensuring peace and tranquillity. It is a haven for young families with a large, safe and imaginatively equipped playground, complemented by a games room with pool table, darts and children's toys. The three homely cottages have been individually designed to provide maximum comfort and absolute privacy. Each has its own private patio with barbecue and garden furniture, while the kitchens are equipped to the very highest standards. The Woodmore Cottage, as befits its name, features exposed beams and a log burning stove. The split-level Brues has a charming galleried landing looking down onto an airy and bright living room and large kitchen area. Ladywell Cottage, the most intimate of the three, is a single storey wooden building which has a wooden-beamed ceiling and log fire. Fitness enthusiasts will enjoy the free membership to Saffron Walden Leisure Centre. The Imperial War Museum, a must for those interested in the history of aviation, is only eight miles away whilst Newmarket racecourse will provide amusement for the more adventurous. A full colour brochure is available on request. **Directions:** From Cambridge, take M11. Exit at junction 8 and follow B1383 to Saffron Walden. From the top of the common take the road to Ashdon. Take the Haverhill turn and continue for 2 miles.

Cottage Name	Sleeps	Bedrooms	Shower	Bath
THE BRUES	8	4	1	1
WOODMORE COTTAGE	6	3	1	1
LADYWELL COTTAGE	4	3	1	1

CANNINGTON (Nr Quantocks Hills)

PRICES

Cottage
from £1500
to £2000
per week

OTHER FACILITIES

Cot available

Shop nearby

Parking facilities

Open Fire

Garden furniture

Barbecue

Bicycle Hire

GRANGE BARN

CANNINGTON, SOMERSET TA5 2LD
TEL: 01278 652216 FAX: 01278 653611 E-MAIL: grangehols@aol.com
OWNERS: Deirdre Hodder-Williams

Dating from the 17th century and set in a lovely private garden, with full use of nearly four acres of adjoining landscaped gardens, a stay in Grange Barn is a delight. The house, approached through imposing iron-clad gates, is a traditional stone barn lavishly converted into a luxury rural hideaway. It exudes countryside charm and promises a level of hospitality typical of deepest Somerset. The gorgeously presented house is awash with antiques. The Oakwood floor and inglenook fireplace in the sitting room and huge circular drawing room create comfort on a grand scale, complemented by the hand-built kitchen with Aga. There are two master bedroom suites, one is fully panelled in wood with traditional Victorian bathroom and the other has beams and a Jacuzzi bath. The picturesque walled garden is tasteful and inviting, offering almost complete privacy. A summerhouse competes for the visitors' attention with a bubbling fountain and the wooden bridge. An ideal family retreat, Grange Barn has its own stylish outdoor pool area with table tennis, it also enjoys full use of the facilites at The Grange (through a private gate), including indoor pool complex with slide, Jacuzzi, sauna and bar. The Quantocks, excellent for walks, hikes and horse riding are only ten minutes drive. With bike hire available, the many cycling routes should not be missed! Within a short drive are Kilve, Exmoor and the beaches of North Somerset, while Glastonbury, Bath and the Cheddar Caves are all within an hour's drive. **Directions:** Exit M5 at junction 23 and head south through Bridgewater. Turn onto A39 in the direction of Minehead for approximately four miles. Grange Barn is just before Cannington on the right hand side of the road.

Cottage Name	Sleeps	Bedrooms	Shower	Bath
GRANGE BARN	12	6	1	2

OLD MILL FARM

POOLE KEYNES, CIRENCESTER, GLOUCESTERSHIRE GL7 6ED
TEL: 01285 821255 FAX: 01285 821531
OWNERS: Gordon and Catherine Hazell

Tupenny, Stable, Granary and Thames are the names of the four holiday cottages situated in a secluded farmyard close to the River Thames in the beautiful Cotswolds countryside. This is a 100 acre arable and sheep farm which will delight young and old alike. Children will particularly enjoy the sights and sounds of Old Mill Farm. All the cottages are barn conversions fitted to a high specification and retaining many of their original and attractive features. These include exposed beams, stone walls and pillars. Each cottage is equipped with all modern facilities from microwave cooker and fridge to colour television, are comfortably furnished and have the additional luxury of full central heating and double glazing. Tupenny and Stable Cottages are adjoining single storey cottages while Granary and the larger Thames, which sleeps seven, are adjoining two storey cottages with balconies from which visitors can admire and enjoy superb views over the river and surrounding countryside. There is a separate laundry room with an automatic machine, tumble dryer and ironing board. Both Thames and Stable Cottages have dishwashers. Old Mill is an ideal centre for touring the enchanting Cotswolds. The delights of Cirencester are just four miles away and Cheltenham, Stratford-upon-Avon and Bath are within easy reach. There is wind-surfing, jet and water skiing, sailing, fishing, horse riding and nature reserves at Cotswold Water Park, a mile away. For the golf enthusiast, Cirencester has a testing 18-hole course. All correspondence must be sent to Ermin House Farm, Syde, Cheltenham, Gloucestershire GL53 5PN. **Directions:** Poole Keynes is 4 miles south west of Cirencester, which is reached by the A419 from junction 15 of the M4.

Cottage Name	Sleeps	Bedrooms	Shower	Bath
TUPENNY	3	1	1	1
STABLE	4	2	1	1
GRANARY	2	1	1	1
THAMES	7	4	1	1

PRICES

Smallest Cottage
from £340
to £735
per week

Largest Cottage
from £560
to £1265
per week

OTHER FACILITIES

Scenic views

Cot available

Shop nearby

Parking facilities

Open Fire

Laundry Service

Prepared meals available

Maid Service

Garden furniture

Barbecue

Children's Play Area

GLADWINS FARM

HARPER'S HILL, NAYLAND, SUFFOLK CO6 4NU
TEL: 01206 262261 FAX: 01206 263001 E-MAIL: GladwinsFarm@compuserve.com
OWNERS: Robert and Pauline Dossor

Offering all the homely comforts that one would expect from one of England's finest retreats, Gladwins Farm lies in 22 acres of lilting Suffolk countryside. At the heart of the Dedham Vale, a bucolic paradise made famous by Constable and Gainsborough, Gladwins offers glorious views of the luscious Stour Valley. The farm is a wonderful place to escape the grind of urban living. The wooded gardens play host to a variety of wildlife, including badgers, bats and owls. Anglers can indulge their passion for fly-fishing in the Farm's lake, whilst their children frolic in the playground. A newly built swimming pool is housed in a spectacular wood-panelled building, where visitors can also enjoy the sauna and aromatherapy suite. The cottages are delightfully redesigned stables with central heating, luxurious suites and televisions. Some benefit from wood fires, illuminating dark and chilly evenings. Chelsworth is a purpose-built luxury cottage with en suite bedrooms. Nearby Nayland, a charming muddle of pastel-coloured cottages, is warm and hospitable. Its pubs and teashops have a laid-back ambience that tempts the visitor into whiling away the tranquil afternoons. Gladwins is ideally positioned to explore the villages of Constable. Dedham, Lavenham, Colchester and the horse races at Newmarket are nearby, while Long Melford's famous antiques shops should not be missed. Colchester, a mere ten minutes drive away, is a bustling town. Historic Cambridge and thriving Norwich are an hour away. **Directions:** From Ipswich, the A12 south. At Colchester take the A134 towards Sudbury for six miles. Gladwins Farm is about 600 metres past the small village of Nayland on the left.

Cottage Name	Sleeps	Bedrooms	Shower	Bath
CONSTABLE	6	3		1
CHELSWORTH	8	4	2	2

A member of
Premier Cottages Direct

ASHELFORD

ASHELFORD, EAST DOWN, NR BARNSTAPLE, NORTH DEVON EX31 4LU
TEL: 01271 850469 FAX: 01271 850862 E-MAIL: tom&erica@ashelford.co.uk
OWNERS: Tom and Erica McClenaghan

Ashelford stands in over 70 acres of superb pasture and woodland at the head of its own valley with views beyond the National Trust's Arlington Court to Exmoor. Formerly a 17th century farmhouse it has retained its sense of history and old world charm with a wealth of oak beams, slate floors and open fires. The converted Exmoor Barn offers unique holiday accommodation many exposed timbers, magnificent open stone fireplace, polished wood floors, luxury bathroom and a fully fitted kitchen with every modern amenity. With its uninterrupted views to Exmoor and suntrap patio overlooking the farm's restful water garden, it provides total luxury for the most discerning visitor. The enchanting two bedrooms, which sleep four, are warmly decorated and extremely well appointed. The four bedrooms in the Farmhouse Wing, which has great charm and character, exude peace and seclusion, and are of a similarly high standard. The sitting room and dining room are snug, comfortable and welcoming and there are excellent cooking facilities. The wing sleeps seven and has three bathrooms. For visitors wishing to escape the chore of cooking, Tom and Erica will gladly provide delicious meals by arrangement. Ashelford is ideal for those wishing to enjoy the surroundings, doing little or nothing, but should they want to be more active, golf, fishing, riding and carriage driving can be arranged. There are also many interesting walks nearby. **Directions:** From Barnstaple take A39 towards Lynmouth. After Shirwell village take the second turning on the left and follow signs to Churchill. Ashelford is on the right.

Cottage Name	Sleeps	Bedrooms	Shower	Bath
THE EXMOOR BARN	4	2	1	1
FARMHOUSE WING	7	4	1	3

PRICES

Smallest Cottage
£1200
per week

Largest Cottage
£1500
per week

OTHER FACILITIES

Scenic views

Parking facilities

Open Fire

Laundry Service

Prepared meals available

Maid Service

Garden furniture

Barbecue

Bicycle Hire

PRICES

Smallest Cottage

from £257
to £579
per week

Largest Cottage

from £495
to £1407
per week

OTHER FACILITIES

Scenic views

Cot available

Parking facilities

Open fire

Garden furniture

Barbecue

Children's Play Area

HIGHER BOWDEN

NR DARTMOUTH, SOUTH DEVON TQ6 0LH
TEL: 01803 770745 FAX: 01803 770262
MANAGERS: Paul and Monica Khosla

Nestling within six acres of attractive grounds, the cottages at Higher Bowden are an ideal retreat for those seeking a peaceful ambience and pleasant surroundings. Located just a mile away from the coast, these two cottages have been carefully converted from former stone farm buildings, whilst retaining the charm of the original properties. The cottages have been individually furnished in order to accentuate their warmth and character. Sleeping six people, Rose Cottage is decorated with comfort in mind and features a range of facilities including a fully fitted kitchen and utility room. Overlooking the attractive pond, stream and waterfall, Garden Cottage has a private terrace for guests to sit and admire the surroundings. There are other cottages on the estate which have not been inspected by Johansens. Fitness enthusiasts will be pleased with the recreational opportunities at Higher Bowden complex. Guests may take a dip in the indoor heated swimming pool and then work out in the newly equipped gymnasium. More relaxing options include a spa bath, sauna and solarium. There are snooker and pool tables and table tennis may be enjoyed. Young children (and their parents) will particularly appreciate the under-5's playroom and the two outdoor playgrounds. The Beech Walk takes guests through the former cider orchard and those with a passion for nature will be pleased to note that Dartmouth, with its abundance of wildlife and rural landscape, is only 4 miles away. A number of sports may be practised in the area such as golf, sailing and fishing. **Directions:** Off A3122 Halwell to Dartmouth road, near Dunkirk Garden Centre, follow brown signs to Fast Rabbit Farm. Higher Bowden is 1 mile past Fast Rabbit.

Cottage Name	Sleeps	Bedrooms	Shower	Bath
ROSE COTTAGE	6	3	1	1
GARDEN COTTAGE	4	2	1	1

THE NETLEY HALL ESTATE

DORRINGTON, SHREWSBURY, SHROPSHIRE SY5 7JZ
TEL: 01743 718339 FAX: 01743 718272 E-MAIL: holiday@netleyhall.co.uk
OWNER: Mr S Lilley

Anyone wanting to feel what it is like to own a large country estate should hurry along to Netley Hall. Here the owners are re-creating a fine Victorian mansion and extend a friendly welcome to guests staying in its varied cottages, inviting them to wander freely over their 150 acres of Shropshire parkland, woods, farmland, formal gardens and fishing lakes. Each cottage is situated in a different part of the estate and each has been carefully decorated and furnished in appropriate colours and styles, while fittings and equipment have been chosen to ensure that the accommodation is outstandingly comfortable both in summer and winter. There are nine cottages on the estate, from the small, cosy, single-storey Old Forge, looking out on to its cobbled yard and the charming Dovecote next to the estate's lovely walled garden, to the characterful 16th century Tythe Barn, with its fine oak beams, offering accommodation for up to 8 people. Fisherman's Cottage sleeps three people and adjoins Tythe Barn. These two cottages can be let as one unit. For those seeking a family holiday for four to six people, there are three other detached cottages each within its own garden and also attractively furnished. Netley Hall Estate lies ten minutes from the Tudor town of Shrewsbury and just four miles from the Shropshire Hills, while within the grounds are six well-stocked fishing lakes. Golf and horse-riding may be enjoyed nearby. **Directions:** From the A49 six miles south of Shrewsbury turn west in Dorrington village into Church Road towards Picklescott. The Netley Hall Estate is one mile away on the left.

Cottage Name	Sleeps	Bedrooms	Shower	Bath
COACHMAN'S COTTAGE	6	3	1	1
THE GATE HOUSE	4	2		1
CAMBRIDGE LODGE	5	4	1	1
THE OLD FORGE	2	1		1
THE DOVECOTE	2	1		1
FISHERMANS COTTAGE	3	2		1
GARDENERS COTTAGE	4	3	1	1
TYTHE BARN	8	3		3
THE BOTHY	2	1		1

HIGHERCOMBE COTTAGE & WING

DULVERTON, SOMERSET TA22 9PT
TEL: 01398 323451
OWNERS: Pam and Hugo Jeune

This gracious, grey-stone, Georgian former hunting lodge and farmhouse has been carefully preserved, tastefully renovated and upgraded to provide a relaxing countryside break. Situated in eight acres of secluded wooded grounds and colourful, lawned gardens in the beautiful Exmoor National Park, Grade II listed Highercombe Cottage offers comfortable and attractive accommodation throughout the year. This includes a delightful, wisteria-clad, three-bedroom cottage which sleeps six and a tastefully presented one bedroom wing accommodating two plus a child. Both have comforting log-burning fires to relax beside, during the colder months. All the bedrooms in the cottage and wing are fully en suite and equipped to the highest standards including central heating, television, tea and coffee making facilities. They also offer magnificent panoramic views over the the stunning flower and shrub-filled grounds which frequently attract the elusive red deer. Highercombe is a peaceful sanctuary and an ideal base for touring, walking, riding, fishing, shooting parties and hunting holidays. It is only 900 yards from open moorland with miles of superb walks and footpaths leading to pretty villages and wooded coombes. Tarr Steps, an ancient causeway across the River Barle, is just two miles away and within easy reach are Dunster's Norman Castle, 17th century Yarn Market, Exmoor Forest and many National Trust houses and gardens. Bed and breakfast is available within the main house and there are several fine pubs nearby which serve excellent lunches and dinners. **Directions:** From Dulverton take the B3223 signed Lynton and Exford. Highercombe is on the right after approximately 2½ miles.

Cottage Name	Sleeps	Bedrooms	Shower	Bath
THE WING	2	1		1
HIGHERCOMBE COTTAGE	6	3	1	2

PRICES

Smallest Cottage
from £290
to £495
per week

Largest Cottage
from £520
to £1120
per week

OTHER FACILITIES

Scenic views

Cot available

Shop nearby

Parking facilities

Open Fire

Laundry Service

Garden furniture

Barbecue

Bicycle Hire

BRIDGE END FARM COTTAGES

BOOT, ESKDALE, THE LAKE DISTRICT, CUMBRIA CA19 1TG
TEL: 01242 679900 FAX: 01242 679911 E-MAIL: greg@cottageholidays.u–net.com
OWNER: Greg Poole

Situated in Eskdale, perhaps the prettiest valley in the Lake District, Bridge End Farm has won many awards including two England for Excellence awards and was voted Best in the Lake District in 1997. It is a collection of Grade II listed cottages dating back to Elizabethan times. Hidden away in the quaint hamlet of Boot, nestling beneath the imposing Scafell Pike, England's highest mountain, the cottages have been imaginatively designed and feature fine granite stonework, oak beams and tasteful furnishings. There are well-maintained walled gardens where visitors can enjoy picnics beside the Whillan Beck with views of some of England's most spectacular countryside. The largest cottage is the Farmhouse, which has recently been given a deluxe 5-star rating. It has stone-flagged floors, oak-beamed ceilings, oak-panelling and an original Jacobean court cupboard. Standing in its own walled garden, it has an attractive country style kitchen and glorious fell views. Stanley Ghyll is simply brimming with personality. A one-bedroomed stone cottage, it has a magnificent oak-fitted kitchen and its own secluded patio. There are other cottages on the estate, please ask for details. Bridge End is an ideal base for walking in the Lake District. From the cottages, guests may hike up to Scafell Pike. The dramatic Wastwater, England's deepest lake, is a pleasant walk from Boot. **Directions:** From M6 take A590 at Jct36. After 20 mins turn right at Workington and Broughton in Furness signpost. Continue past Broughton, turn right at traffic lights just before Duddon Bridge. Go through Ulpha, turn left for Eskdale. In Eskdale turn right at signpost for Boot. Turn left into the village at the Brook House Inn. Bridge End is at far end of village, next to the 17th C packhorse bridge.

Cottage Name	Sleeps	Bedrooms	Shower	Bath
THE FARMHOUSE	8	4	2	2
STANLEY GHYLL COTTAGE	2	1	1	1

PRICES

Smallest Cottage

from £250
to £500
per week

Largest Cottage

from £290
to £530
per week

OTHER FACILITIES

Scenic views

Cot available

Parking facilities

Laundry Service

Prepared meals available

Garden furniture

Barbecue

BARKHAM

SANDYWAY, SOUTH MOLTON, NORTH DEVON EX36 3LU
TEL/FAX: 01643 831370 E-MAIL: adie.exmoor@btinternet.com
OWNERS: John and Penny Adie

This is a truly idyllic location, nestling within 12 acres of parkland and woods with waterfalls and streams meandering along the undulating lawns and vales. Situated within the Exmoor National Park, Barkham comprises a traditional farmhouse dominated by an attractive courtyard and three modern cottages. Taking their names from the fields surrounding the house, the cottages are impressive conversions from two 18th century stone barns and feature an array of the latest facilities. The Old Copse is well-appointed with antiques and fine décor and guests may relax in either the sitting room or, in finer months, on the small patio. The same high standards of furnishings and amenities may be enjoyed at Turnip Close and Dobbin's Close. All of the cottages offer a well-equipped kitchen and breakfast area.

Those seeking a break from the kitchen will enjoy the freshly prepared meals which are available in the oak-panelled dining room in the main house by arrangement. The packed lunches are popular with day-trippers. The premises are also licensed to serve alcoholic beverages. There is a large beamed gallery displaying beautiful paintings by the owner himself and other artists. Pastimes include riding and salmon and trout fishing in season. Those with a penchant for countryside walks will enjoy the many interesting and adventurous routes nearby whilst music lovers will be pleased with the many concerts that take place here. Barkham is 15 miles from the sea and theme parks and National Trust properties abound. **Directions:** Contact Barkham for detailed directions.

Cottage Name	Sleeps	Bedrooms	Shower	Bath
DOBBINS CLOSE	6	3		1
TURNIP CLOSE	4	2		1
OLD COPSE	5	3		1

PRICES

Smallest Cottage

from £246
to £498
per week

Largest Cottage

from £441
to £1098
per week

OTHER FACILITIES

Scenic views

Cot available

Shop nearby

Parking facilities

Prepared meals available

Maid Service

Garden furniture

Barbecue

Bicycle Hire

Children's Play Area

VERE LODGE

SOUTH RAYNHAM, FAKENHAM, NORFOLK NR21 7HE
TEL: 01328 838261 FAX: 01328 838300
OWNERS: Major and Mrs George Bowlby

Spacious and beautifully decorated self-contained cottages are scattered in seclusion throughout eight acres of woodlands, paddocks and sweeping lawns surrounding impressive Vere Lodge, a Grade II listed building dating from 1798 and former dower house to Raynham Hall. Some are conversions of old outbuildings, others recently built. All have every home comfort. Families are particularly well catered for. The grounds are a paradise for children with a playground, a toddlers' play area and unusually tame rabbits, hens, peacocks, dogs, goats, a donkey and a pony to stroke, feed and enjoy. A grass tennis court and croquet lawn cater for the sports enthusiast and a leisure centre with a 38-foot-long swimming pool, sauna, solarium, table tennis, pool table, sun patios, lounge and an occasional bar serving drinks and alfresco snacks are in a corner of the grounds so as not to intrude upon the peace and seclusion of Vere Lodge. Fresh free-range eggs and a selection of mainly home-cooked foods can be obtained in the leisure centre and there is a launderette. This is a delightful property throughout the seasons: in winter a warm ambience envelopes the lodge and the summer months offer a plethora of outdoor opportunities. There are twelve other cottages available, please enquire for further details. Three night breaks are available. The varied places of interest nearby include historic properties such as Blickling Hall, Holkham Hall, Sandringham. Guests may walk along the sandy beaches whilst riding and fishing can be arranged. **Directions:** From Swaffham take A1065 towards Fakenham. After 11 miles enter South Raynham: 100 yards past the village sign turn left. Vere Lodge is the white house 400 yards ahead.

Cottage Name	Sleeps	Bedrooms	Shower	Bath
DOLLS HOUSE	4	2	1	1
ROSE COTTAGE	7	4	1	1

RUDDING HOLIDAY PARK

FOLLIFOOT, HARROGATE, NORTH YORKSHIRE HG3 1JH
TEL: 01423 870439 FAX: 01423 870859 E-MAIL: holidaypark@rudding–park.co.uk
OWNERS: Mackaness Family

Surrounded by 50 acres of beautiful parkland, landscaped gardens and woodland walks in the heart of North Yorkshire, Rudding Park forms part of a private country estate owned and run by the same family since 1972. Nestling in and around the estate are nine traditional country cottages of mellow stone or warm red brick. All have been carefully restored, retain many of their original features and have spectacular views over their surrounds and some of the most delightful countryside in the country. Each is is comfortably furnished and fully equipped with high quality fittings and utensils. They include colour television, iron and ironing board, vacuum cleaner, washing machine, electric heaters, fridge and pay-phone. Some of the larger cottages have an automatic washing machine, tumble dryer, fridge freezer and dishwasher. Central heating is standard but some cottages also have open log fires. Pastimes include walks through the woodlands and rhododendron filled gardens which are shared with Rudding Park House and Hotel. Outdoor facilities include a heated outdoor swimming pool with sun patio and children's paddling pool, an adventure park for the youngsters, a superb 18-hole golf course and an 18 bay floodlit driving range. Cycles can be hired and horse riding, fishing and shooting can be arranged nearby. Rudding Park is just three miles from the lovely spa town of Harrogate and within easy reach of the quaint market town of Knaresborough, historic Ripon with its magnificent cathedral, Fountains Abbey, the Lightwater Valley Theme Park and the delights of the unspoilt Dales. **Directions:** Follifoot is just off the A658 between its junction with the A61 to Leeds and the A661 to Wetherby. Follow the signs to Rudding Park.

Cottage Name	Sleeps	Bedrooms	Shower	Bath
NORTH LODGE	6	3		1
GARDENER'S COTTAGE	6	3	1	1
BOTHY COTTAGE	7	3		1
KEEPER'S COTTAGE	10	4	2	1
GUN ROOM	2	1	1	
CLARO COTTAGE	3	1		1
BEAGLE COTTAGE	3	1		1
DUCKS NEST FARM	7	3		1
DUCKS NEST GRANARY	4	2		1
DUCKS NEST LOFT	2	1		1

PRICES

Smallest Cottage
from £270
to £400
per week

Largest Cottage
from £425
to £810
per week

OTHER FACILITIES

Scenic views

Cot available

Shop nearby

Parking facilities

Open Fire

Laundry Service

Garden furniture

Barbecue

Bicycle Hire

DOWNE COTTAGES

HARTLAND, NORTH DEVON EX39 6DA
TEL: 01237 441881 FAX: 01237 441881 E-MAIL: jeremy@downefarm.demon.co.uk
OWNERS: Jeremy and Lynda Roe

Located within a designated area of outstanding beauty, Downe Cottages is a charming collection of five listed Victorian barns that have been tastefully renovated. Each of the cottages has its own personality and character and guarantees visitors absolute peace and seclusion. Tastefully appointed and immaculately presented, the cottages offer the height of modern convenience and comfort and are truly spacious. Every bedroom has an en suite bathroom. Much of the pine furniture has been by local artisans, while all the cottages have oil-fired central heating and, where allowed, an open fire. Wistaria, sleeping a maximum of six, is the largest of the cottages. Occupying the whole of what was once a large barn, it is set on two floors with a pretty galleried landing and open plan living room. Clematis Cottage, with one bedroom, has captivating views over the sea to Lundy Island. The open plan ground floor contains the living, dining and kitchen areas with the bedroom occupying the second floor. Ivy Cottage is a spacious two-bedroom cottage that also has magnificent sea views through its French windows. There are other cottages on the estate; please ask for details. The surrounding area is a paradise for walkers and cyclists. The cliff-top walks are truly bewitching. Visitors speak of the sense of complete isolation as they stumble upon the many secluded coves. There are several golf courses in the vicinity, and Downe can arrange sea and lake fishing. **Directions:** Exit M5 at junction 25. Take A361 to Barnstaple following A39 towards Bideford then Bude. Turn right onto B2348 after Clovelly Cross. Through Hartland towards Hartland Quay, turn right towards Berry. Follow the single track over the stone bridge. Downe is on the left.

Cottage Name	Sleeps	Bedrooms	Shower	Bath
WISTARIA COTTAGE	6	3	3	
CLEMATIS COTTAGE	2	1	1	
IVY COTTAGE	4	2	2	

PLANTATION HOUSE

YARMOUTH, ISLE OF WIGHT

C/O RURAL RETREATS TEL: 01386 701177 FAX: 01386 701178 E-MAIL: info@ruralretreats.co.uk
OWNERS: Christine and David Jones

A substantially refurbished holiday property built in the 1930s, Plantation House is a stunning waterfront property with remarkable views of the Solent. Set in one and a half acres of secluded wooded gardens, its 360 foot frontage onto the Solent make it a paradise for lovers of watersports. Visitors enter the house via a wide verandah with the rooms being set out on three floors. The interior contains many of the buildings original features, including high-beamed ceilings, wooden blinds and open fireplaces throughout. The reception room, with its sumptuous furniture, gives the visitor a truly panoramic view from Lymington to the Solent. The bedrooms, decorated in the manner of Frank Lloyd Wright, are spacious and refined. Hardwood floors, Victorian blinds and high ceilings set the lavish and elegant tone. The two master en suite bedrooms both have three aspect views of the Solent. Plantation House also has an enclosed kitchen garden and orchard with apple, plum and mirabelle trees. Swimming is possible from cottage's harbour jetty. Plantation House is a picturesque 15 minute stroll from the historic town of Yarmouth, with its many vibrant bars and restaurants and popular harbour. To the east lies Newton Creek, a medieval village and bird sanctuary, preserved by the National Trust. Also in the vicinity are the Tennyson Trail and Needles, which provide some of the most dramatic coastal walks in England. Please enquire for three night stay. Prices on application. **Directions:** From the Lymington/Yarmouth ferry, follow the coast road east.

Cottage Name	Sleeps	Bedrooms	Shower	Bath
PLANTATION HOUSE	8	4		3

DERWENT MANOR

PORTINSCALE, KESWICK, CUMBRIA CA12 5RE
TEL: 017687 72211 FAX: 017687 71002 E-MAIL: derwentwater.hotel@dial.pipex.com
OWNERS: Diment Ltd

Tucked away in Portinscale village on the northern tip of Derwentwater in the heart of the Lake District, Derwent Manor provides welcoming, comfortable accommodation. The manor, at one time the country residence of Alderman John Graves, three times Lord Mayor of Manchester, stands just across a lane from its owners' hotel, the Derwentwater, so that guests may also enjoy the hotel's 16 acres of gardens and meadows leading towards the lake. The manor has been attractively refurbished to offer a variety of self-catering apartments, all furnished and equipped to a high standard and each provided with dishwasher, TV, video and CD player. Buttermere, an apartment on the ground floor, sleeps two in a twin-bedded room and features large bay windows looking on to the garden. On the first floor, Dunmail's two double bedrooms each have an en suite bathroom, while there is a well-appointed dining room and separate sitting-room with views towards the lake. Fairfield, another two-bedroomed apartment, is on the second floor, with windows looking on to the fells. Hidden away in the manor's grounds is Glaramara Cottage. Here guests can enjoy the privacy of their own patio. The ground floor offers a roomy kitchen and a lounge room, while the first-floor bedroom has a half-tester bed, and separate dressing area. There are other cottages on the estate which have not been inspected by Johansens. All around lies the glorious lakeland countryside teeming with wildlife, while a 20 minute walk along an attractive path brings one to the bustling little town of Keswick. **Directions:** Turn off M6 at Jct. 40, westwards on to A66. By-pass Keswick and after about 1 mile, turn left into Portinscale. Follow signposts to Derwentwater Hotel.

Cottage Name	Sleeps	Bedrooms	Shower	Bath
GLARAMARA COTTAGE	2	1	1	1
FAIRFIELD	4	2	1	1
DUNMAIL	4	2	2	2
BUTTERMERE	2	1	1	1

A member of
Premier Cottages Direct

TREWORGEY COTTAGES

DULOE, LISKEARD, CORNWALL PL14 4PP
TEL: 01503 262730 FAX: 01503 263757 E-MAIL: treworgey@enterprise.net
OWNERS: Bevis and Linda Wright

These delightful Cornish cottages are idyllic holiday homes for those seeking peace and seclusion, for those with romance in their hearts, or for those just wanting to soak up atmosphere and relax amidst pleasant surroundings. Built in the 18th century and family run, Treworgey Cottages offer the comfort of a first class hotel with freedom and escapism from the stresses of today's town and city life. Owners Bevis and Linda Wright guarantee quality personal service and really welcome families and pets throughout the year. They even provide superb home cooked meals for those wanting to take a day off from the fully-equipped kitchen. Surrounded by the beauty of the Looe Valley and Looe River and with breathtaking, unspoilt views, Treworgey's cottages have everything. Roses around the doors, beamed ceilings and restful, individual private gardens enhance the properties.

All the cottages are tastefully decorated and carefully furnished with antiques, fine furnishings and deep, soft sofas and armchairs. Open log fires in winter months add to the sense of comfort and cosiness. Various cottages have from one to four bedrooms with four-poster beds and sleep from two to eight. Activities include swimming, riding and helping to look after Treworgey's horses, or spotting wildlife in the countryside. Animals are a big attraction here and children are encouraged to join in with feeding times and grooming. There are miles of walking to be enjoyed along the National Trust coastline and the harbour and smugglers museum at Polperro to explore. Specialities at Treworgey include romantic breaks and honeymoons. **Directions:** Treworgey is near Sandplace and is located 5 miles south of Liskeard on B3254 road and 2 miles from Looe.

Cottage Name	Sleeps	Bedrooms	Shower	Bath
COOMBE FARMHOUSE	7/8	4	1	1
ELM COTTAGE	4	2	1	1
HOLLYHOCK COTTAGE	2	1		1

PRICES

Smallest Cottage

from £306
to £485
per week

Largest Cottage

from £585
to £1158
per week

OTHER FACILITIES

Scenic views

Cot available

Parking facilities

Open Fire

Prepared meals available

Garden furniture

Barbecue

CHAMPERNHAYES

WOOTTON FITZPAINE, BRIDPORT, DORSET DT6 6DF
TEL: 01297 560853 FAX: 01297 561155 E-MAIL: champhayes@aol.com
OWNERS: Elaine and Derek Thompson

Perched on the slope of a West Dorset hillside and surrounded by lush woodland and verdant Dorset fields, Champernhayes is a 15th century farmhouse providing the highest quality of self-catering. The cottages skillfully combine the ambience of the original buildings with modern comfort and luxury. Each has its own private garden, complete with barbecue and patio furniture and magnificent open plan sitting rooms tastefully designed in the style of modern France. While visitors share a common heated pool, two of the cottages have their own pools guaranteeing shelter and privacy. The kitchens have also been tastefully designed, well-equipped and are bathed in soothing pastel shades. With en suite bathrooms and reconditioned antique bedframes, visitors can spend their nights in true opulence. Short breaks are available from October to April. A short drive from the sea, Champernhayes is ideally located to explore the stunning Dorset coastline. The charming historic town of Lyme Regis, a mere three miles away, has golden beaches, a pretty harbour and excellent windsurfing and watersports. Two miles away lies Charmouth, the epicentre of the Heritage coastline, where visitors can stroll along spectacular cliffs where unique fossils abound. The region is a hiker's paradise. The famous Dorset coastal path offers walks to suit all, while those with a penchant for history can follow the so-called Liberty Trail, the path of the 1685 Monmouth Rebellion. **Directions:** From Dorchester, take the A35, turning left to Charmouth. Pass through Wootton Fitzpaine and follow the signs.

Cottage Name	Sleeps	Bedrooms	Shower	Bath
L'ALOUETTE	4	2	2	2
L'HIBOU	4	2	2	1
LE MERLE	6	3	3	3
L'HIRONDELLE	3	1	1	1
CHAMPERNHAYES FARMHOUSE	8	4	2	3

PRICES

Smallest Cottage

from £327
to £579
per week

Largest Cottage

from £552
to £1257
per week

OTHER FACILITIES

Scenic views

Cot available

Shop nearby

Parking facilities

Open Fire

Garden furniture

Barbecue

Bicycle Hire

HOPTON HALL

HOPTON, WIRKSWORTH, DERBYSHIRE DE4 4DF
TEL: 01629 540458 FAX: 01629 540712 E-MAIL: H.E@sagnet.co.uk
OWNERS: Bill and Eddy Brogden

Hopton Hall stands tall and majestically in the heart of 30 acres of grounds and woodlands deep in the Derbyshire Dales surrounded by spectacular peaks and crags, fine old manor houses, Norman churches and stone circles. It is a magnificent wooded countryside rich in history and archaeology with Wirksworth famous for its annual Whitsun well-dressing ceremony as well as for being a Roman lead-mining centre. The Hall's attractive cobbled courtyard of listed stables, coach house and servants cottages have been beautifully transformed into five comfortable, spacious and individually styled cottages sleeping from four to ten. All are delightfully decorated and furnished, have central heating and fully equipped modern kitchens that include dishwasher, washing machine/dryer and microwave. Many of the cottages feature their original oak beams and have open log fires. Three have private and secluded small gardens in which to relax during summer months. The Hall's grounds include a paddock and barbecue tables, football and volleyball facilities and there is a popular children's play area with swings, slide and climbing frame. Clay pigeon and shooting can be arranged and at Carsington Water, which virtually adjoins the property, there is an abundance of watersports, including windsurfing, canoeing, sailing, and fishing, and a bird sanctuary. Alton Towers, the Great American Adventure, Gullivers Kingdom and Abraham's Heights are all close by. The prices are exclusive of energy charges. **Directions:** Exit M1 at junction 28 and follow A38 to Alfreton. Then take A615 to Matlock and from there A6 and B5035 to Wirksworth and Hopton.

Cottage Name	Sleeps	Bedrooms	Shower	Bath
THE OLDE HAYBARN	4	2	1	1
GARDNER'S COTTAGE	8	4	2	2
DOVE COTE	4	2	1	1
THE BUTLER'S QUARTERS	10	5	2	2
HOPTON CLOSE	8	4	1	2

BEACON HILL FARM

LONGHORSLEY, MORPETH, NORTHUMBERLAND NE65 8QW
TEL/FAX: 01670 788372
OWNER: Clare Moore

Pinioned by the sweeping countryside of the Cheviot Hills and the brooding Northumbrian coastline, Beacon Hill Farm's unhindered views bring calm to the soul. Set on a 350 acre grass farm with a 40 acre Beech wood, a haven for a wide array of birds and animals, it is a truly idyllic location to escape the rigours of the modern world. The cottages are all beautifully appointed and visitors are constantly impressed by the stunning views from the sitting rooms and the large quantities of books, lamps and pictures that adorn the walls. There is also a luxurious 40 foot heated swimming pool housed in a building with a charmingly slated roof, complete with sauna, solarium and a large gymnasium. Quarry House, perhaps the finest of the cottages, is a totally private and secluded single storey sandstone building, with an

antique-laden and spacious drawing room. Elm Cottage is one of two charming stone cottages. Totally open plan, it offers some of the most striking views of the Cheviot Hills. There are other cottages on the estate, please ask for details. Beacon Hill Farm is the ideal place from which to explore the many natural delights that Northumberland has to offer. The imperious Hadrian's Wall, a World Heritage Site, runs from Newcastle to Carlisle. Durham, with its magnificent cathedral, is nearby, while Cragside and Wallington House, both National Trust properties, are both within 10 miles of the Farm. The Farne Islands are also worth a visit. **Directions:** From Newcastle, take the A1, skirting around Morpeth, take the left hand turn with Hebron on the right. Follow the signs.

Cottage Name	Sleeps	Bedrooms	Shower	Bath
QUARRY HOUSE	6	3	1	1
ELM COTTAGE	4	2		1

A member of Premier Cottages Direct

PRICES

Smallest Cottage
from £295
to £625
per week

Largest Cottage
from £720
to £2075
per week

OTHER FACILITIES

Scenic views

Cot available

Shop nearby

Parking facilities

Open Fire

Laundry Service

Prepared meals available

Maid Service

Garden furniture

Barbecue

Bicycle Hire

THE GREAT ESCAPE HOLIDAY COMPANY

DOCKING, KINGS LYNN, NORFOLK
TEL: 01485 518717 FAX: 01485 518937 E-MAIL: holidays@greatescapes.demon.co.uk

The north-west Norfolk coast, sweeping towards the Wash consists mainly of a long stretch of sand and low cliffs, exposed saltings and tidal inlets. There are picturesque little harbours and villages whose houses are built of pebble flint or brown sandstone, an abundance of birdlife, marshland stretching from King's Lynn westwards into Lincolnshire and peace and quiet. It is a place where, one can believe that time really does stands still. Scattered along the coastline are a variety of unique and charming Great Escape holiday homes that are as diverse as they are individual, all of which can help the visitor unwind from the pressures of everyday life. There are grand country houses that can be particularly attractive for corporate gatherings, charming and secluded little cottages, fascinating period houses and airy barn conversions. Some have large gardens leading down to

the marshes and boats are available for use. Others have a sunny patio, a studio or stables waiting for riding guests. The common denominator is the quality and style of the décor, furnishings and service. On arrival guests are personally welcomed and provided with wine and the ingredients for a simple meal. Ready cooked meals may be pre-selected and stored in the freezer. Spotless white bed and bath linen together with a first class maid service all ensure a perfect home-from-home environment. As well as enjoying the sand, sea, watersports and exploring the marshes there are many attractions in the area, including nature reserves, 18th century Holkham Hall and Sandringham. The Company has other cottages which have not been inspected by Johansens. **Directions:** All properties are within easy reach of A149 coast road.

Cottage Name	Sleeps	Bedrooms	Shower	Bath
TURRET HOUSE	7	3		2
BLUE TILES	10	5		4
SCOTTS	10	5		3
MISSION HALL	2	1		1
GLAVEN FARM BARN	2	1		1
SAND PIPER	6	2		2

PRICES

Smallest Cottage
from £215
to £310
per week

Largest Cottage
from £455
to £780
per week

OTHER FACILITIES

Scenic views

Cot available

Shop nearby

Parking facilities

Laundry Service

Maid Service

Garden furniture

OWLPEN MANOR

NR ULEY, GLOUCESTERSHIRE GL11 5BZ
TEL: 01453 860261 FAX: 01453 860819
OWNERS: Nicholas and Karin Mander

This is a dream holiday hamlet tucked away in a steep wooded valley, deep in the heart of the picturesque Cotswolds. The unforgettable surroundings comprise acres of park, rough meadows and wild extensive bluebell woods. Delightful, distinctive period cottages are scattered along the valley floor. There are medieval barns and byres, a watermill first restored in 1464 and former weavers and keepers homes, all having been carefully restored by owners Nicholas and Karin Mander. Centre of the estate is the majestic, Grade I listed Tudor Manor House which overlooks 16th-century formal gardens with hanging terraces and, perhaps, the oldest complete domestic garden in England. The fairytale style cottages have every modern amenity and comfort, including maid service on request. Peter's Nest is the original tiny cottage of Woodwells farmstead, marked on an 1847 map. It sleeps two in an attic bedroom and has a small garden. Manor Farm is built in traditional Cotswold style with gables and mullioned windows, has a Hepplwhite four-poster and sleeps four in two bedrooms. Marlings End nestles below hanging beech woods and also has an old cottage garden. Hidden at the bottom of the valley is ancient Grist Mill. Sleeping nine, it has comfort, style, character and charm with many features of the old mill preserved. These include the huge mill-wheel and pond. There are other cottages on the estate which have not been inspected by Johansens. **Directions:** From the M4, exit at junction 17 or 18 and take the A4135 signed Dursley. After the A46 crossroads take the second fork on the right into Uley. Owlpen is signposted on the right of the green. From the M5 exit at junction 13 or 14 and take the B4066 to Uley.

Cottage Name	Sleeps	Bedrooms	Shower	Bath
PETERS NEST COTTAGE	2	1		1
MANOR FARM	4	2	1	
MARLINGS END	6	3	1	1
GRIST MILL	9	4		2

PRICES

Smallest Cottage

from £192 to £393 per week

Largest Cottage

from £216 to £473 per week

OTHER FACILITIES

Scenic views

Cot available

Shop nearby

Parking facilities

Laundry Service

Maid Service

Garden furniture

STAFFIELD HALL

KIRKOSWALD, PENRITH, CUMBRIA CA10 1EU
TEL: 01768 898656
OWNERS: Beverley and Alan Dawson

Once the seat of local Lords, Staffield Hall is a striking and gracious red sandstone manor house that has been rescued from decline by resident owners Beverley and Alan Dawson. With its tall tower topped by five coats of arms, solid oak front door and soaring chimney stacks it provides a historic and charming setting for a range of attractive and comfortable self-contained apartments. All have four poster beds, all have an impressive range of quality furnishings, fitments and equipment, central heating to keep visitors cosy and warm on the coldest days and nights and magnificent views over extensive grounds and gardens. The apartments are on the first and second floors of the manor and are reached by a grand central stairway over which is a huge stained glass window and a magnificent chandelier. Thick stone walls separate the apartments and the floors are soundproofed for even greater peace and quiet. In the Great Hall, with its ornate ceilings, there is a well stocked library area and a carved stone fireplace to add to the warm and friendly welcome offered by Beverley and Alan. Interesting, relaxing walks are a feature of the 2½ acres of grounds with their terraced lawns, fountain and abundant wildlife. The surrounding countryside offers a number of attractions, including golf, shooting, riding, fishing and a network of lanes and footpaths. **Directions:** Exit the M6 at junction 41 and take the B5305 Carlisle road to Stoneybeck roundabout and the A6. Turn north to Plumpton and then take the B6413 through Lazonby into Kirkoswald. Go straight on towards Armathwaite and after about a mile you reach Staffield village and the Hall on your left.

Cottage Name	Sleeps	Bedrooms	Shower	Bath
HEAVENFIELD	4	2		1
KING OSWALD	5	2		1
THE TOWER	2	1	1	1
LADY TOWER	2	1		1
NURSERY	2	1	1	1
GARDEN OF EDEN	2	1		1

PRICES

Smallest Cottage

from £230 to £540 per week

Largest Cottage

from £440 to £1015 per week

BROOMHILL MANOR

POUGHILL, BUDE, CORNWALL EX23 9HA
TEL: 01288 352940 FAX: 01288 356526 E-MAIL: chris@broomhillmanor.co.uk
OWNERS: Chris and Rowena Mower

Set in the enchanting region of Cornwall on the outskirts of Bude, Broomhill Manor is a delight throughout the seasons. The area is awash with colour as snowdrops, violets and daffodils welcome the new spring whilst the autumnal beauty of the landscape with its hazy sunsets and golden and russet hues is unforgettable. Broomhill is the ideal venue in which to escape from the pressures of a hectic lifestyle as it is entirely self-contained and has been designed in the style of a small village, thus creating a relaxed, informal atmosphere. Situated in the west wing of the Manor House is an opulent apartment which is truly the essence of comfort. Attractive furnishings and soft fabrics are complemented by an array of modern amenities. The Round House is a former gate keeper's cottage and is still located by an entrance to the estate.

The house has been fashioned in a most unusual and intriguing style and is dominated by a winding staircase leading to the two bedrooms. There are other cottages on the estate, please ask for details. Broomhill offers a variety of pastimes and activities such as swimming in the attractive heated indoor pool or relaxing in the sauna or Jacuzzi. The fully equipped gymnasium and solarium add to the property's health and fitness facilities and a bar and a full-sized snooker table are perfect for relaxing and meeting friends. Horses are an integral part of Broomhill's heritage and guests have exclusive use of the stables. New riders may have lessons whilst the more experienced may try some of the many riding terrains. **Directions:** Take M5 to Exeter, then A30 past Okehampton. Exit onto A3097 through Holsworthy and towards Bude.

OTHER FACILITIES

- Scenic views
- Cot available
- Shop nearby
- Parking facilities
- Laundry Service
- Maid Service
- Garden furniture
- Barbecue
- Bicycle Hire
- Children's Play Area

Cottage Name	Sleeps	Bedrooms	Shower	Bath
MANOR HOUSE APARTMENT	6	3	1	2
THE ROUND HOUSE	2	2	1	1

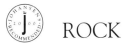

ROCK

PRICES

Smallest Cottage

from £310
to £1115
per week

Largest Cottage

from £515
to £1770
per week

OTHER FACILITIES

Scenic views

Cot available

Shop nearby

Parking facilities

Open fire

Garden furniture

Barbecue

Bicycle Hire

CANT COVE

CANT FARM, ROCK, NR WADEBRIDGE, CORNWALL PL27 6RL
TEL: 01208 862841 FAX: 01208 862142
OWNERS: J.H. Hudson & Son Ltd.

Surrounded by 70 acres of prime countryside, the Cornish coastline, landscaped grounds and woodlands, Cant Cove offers peace and tranquillity for those seeking a break from the pressures of a hectic lifestyle. The six cottages afford breathtaking views across the gardens which are floodlit at night. All are equipped to the highest of standards and feature whirlbaths, power showers, log fires, utility rooms, private patios, barbecues and many other amenities. The Farmhouse and The Granary boast the additional luxury of a sauna; perfect for lazing after a busy day out on the Cornish coast. Superb walks have been created through the attractive grounds which lead down to Cant Cove and wildlife enthusiasts may admire the foxes and badgers. Opportunities for watersports abound and sailing, windsurfing and water-skiing may be practised.

Those wishing to keep their feet on the ground can enjoy tennis, croquet and golf on the 9-hole practise course. Day excursions to St Enodoc Church, the burial place of Sir John Betjeman, are particularly popular and guests may also choose to spend their afternoons exploring the numerous National Trust properties in the area. Sun-worshippers must simply lie back and enjoy the pleasures of some of the cleanest sandy beaches in Europe. With its burning log fires and tranquil surroundings, Cant Cove is ideal for winter breaks or celebrating special occasions. **Directions:** From Wadebridge, join the B3314 and follow the signs to Rock. Carry on for approximately 2 miles and turn left towards Pityme. Continue past 'Cornish Crabbers' and carry on for one mile. Cant Cove is straight ahead.

Cottage Name	Sleeps	Bedrooms	Shower	Bath
KATE	5	3	2	1
ISABELLA	5	3	1	2
ORCHARD HOUSE	6	3	1	2
THE OLD BARN	5	3	1	1
THE FARMHOUSE	6	3	2	2
THE GRANARY	8	4	3	2

PRICES

Smallest Cottage

from £250
to £639
per week

Largest Cottage

from £365
to £990
per week

OTHER FACILITIES

Scenic views

Cot available

Parking facilities

Laundry Service

Maid Service

Garden furniture

Barbecue

Children's Play Area

WREA HEAD COTTAGE HOLIDAYS

WREA HEAD HOUSE, BARMOOR LANE, SCALBY, SCARBOROUGH, NORTH YORKSHIRE YO13 0PG
TEL: 01723 375844 FAX: 01723 500274 E-MAIL: winners@wreaheadcotghols.demon.co.uk
OWNERS: Chris and Andrea Wood

Visitors to Wrea Head cannot help but be impressed by its idyllic setting and the magnificence of the surrounding countryside which offers panoramic views seawards across rolling meadows towards Scarborough and its 12th century castle. Attractively converted from red brick and pantile farm buildings the collection of cottages offer peace and tranquillity and hospitable owners Chris and Andrea Wood have had their hard work honoured with the English Tourist Board's 'England for Excellence Award' and the Yorkshire Tourist Board's 'White Rose Award' for the best self-catering holiday. Extensive lawned gardens, a summerhouse, landscaped courtyard, flower-filled rainbutts and ivy clad walls enhance Wrea Head's charm and character. The cottages, which are open all year, are equipped to the highest standard and include attractively co-ordinated Dorma or Sanderson furnishings, gas central heating, fully fitted kitchens, baths, showers and many other amenities. There is the added luxury of an indoor heated pool, a Jacuzzi and Swedish sauna. For children there is an adventure playground and a Teddy Bears Cottage - complete with Daddy, Mummy and Baby Bear - situated in its own picnic park and play area. Maid and baby sitting services are available. There are other cottages on the estate which have not been inspected by Johansens. Walking enthusiasts can enjoy quiet lanes behind Wrea Head which lead to the lovely Forge Valley, Harwood Dale and Dalby Forest. **Directions:** From Scarborough, take A171 towards Whitby. At Scalby turn left into Barmoor Lane. Go past pond on your right then after ¼ mile Wrea Head House is on your left.

Cottage Name	Sleeps	Bedrooms	Shower	Bath
HAYBARN COTTAGE	8	3	2	1
MEADOW VIEW COTTAGE	4	2	1	1
GRANARY COTTAGE	6	3	1	1

SHERFORD (Nr Kingsbridge)

PRICES

Smallest Cottage

from £486 to £951 per week

Largest Cottage

from £525 to £1124 per week

OTHER FACILITIES

Scenic views

Cot available

Parking facilities

Open Fire

Garden furniture

Barbecue

VALLEY SPRINGS

SHERFORD, NR KINGSBRIDGE, SOUTH DEVON TQ7 2BG
TEL: 01548 531574 FAX: 01548 531574
OWNERS: John Bishop and Lynne Bentley

Valley Springs is idyllically situated in 22 acres of grounds and gardens, bordered by the soft, undulating countryside of the South Hams, just inland from Slapton Sands and its Ley nature reserve. It is an area of outstanding natural beauty, peace and tranquillity. Wild flora and fauna abound while inside the Valley's wooded grounds sub-tropical and rare plants enhance displays of more traditional shrubs and flowers in the floodlit gardens. A nature trail meanders through a bluebell wood down to a tinkling brook and two fishing lakes. The stone cottages, converted from farm buildings, nestle round a spring-fed duck pond and combine the comforts of the 21st century with a rural setting. They are extremely spacious, tastefully furnished and well equipped. Each has a large living room with woodburner, TV and video, a family-size fully equipped kitchen with microwaves, dishwashers and washerdriers, luxurious master bedrooms have en suite facilities and televisions. Each cottage has a payphone. Brown Trout Cottage has a baby grand piano (Challen tuned). There are two other cottages on the estate which have not been inspected by Johansens. Valley Springs has a superb heated indoor swimming pool, sauna and solarium and for the sporting visitors carp or trout fishing in the lakes and clay pigeon shooting can usually be arranged on site. The market town of Kingsbridge and the Salcombe estuary are just a 15 minute drive away and several National Trust properties are within easy reach. **Directions:** From Totnes, join the A381 towards Kingsbridge and follow the brown tourist signs for Valley Springs Fishery.

Cottage Name	Sleeps	Bedrooms	Shower	Bath
BADGER COTTAGE	6	3	2	2
BROWN TROUT COTTAGE	4	2	1	1

PRICES

Smallest Cottage

from £272
to £455
per week

Largest Cottage

from £479
to £838
per week

OTHER FACILITIES

Scenic views

Cot available

Shop nearby

Parking facilities

Open fire

Laundry Service

Prepared meals available

Garden furniture

Barbecue

Bicycle Hire

THE KINGSTON ESTATE

STAVERTON, TOTNES, DEVON TQ9 6AR
TEL: 01803 762235 FAX: 01803 762444 E-MAIL: info@kingston–estate.demon.co.uk
OWNERS: Michael and Elizabeth Corfield

Tucked away in the heart of the lilting hills and valleys of the breathtaking South Hams in South Devon, the Kingston Estate promises visitors a range of individual cottages in a truly idyllic setting. Tantalisingly positioned between Dartmoor and the magnificent Devon coastline, the individually crafted cottages, many listed Grade II, exude the comfort and taste that one would expect of an award-winning estate. All of the cottages are appointed in their own unique style. Two, however, stand out from the rest. Bass Court, a former farm building dating from the 1650s, is set in its own private cobbled courtyard and its charming ambience is enhanced by its quaint galleried landing. The Old Stables, part of the 18th century break front coach house, has a beautiful kitchen which is entered via an arch from the sitting room. Both the cottages feature attractive bedrooms, full electric heating, washing machines and a well-equipped kitchen with all modern appliances. For guests desiring a rest from the kitchen, the Dining Room offers sophisticated cuisine to International standards for adults only, using fresh local ingredients. During the Summer, The Undercroft is opened according to demand to provide high quality, but simpler menus for adults and children. The wine list, boasting over 60 wines from all corners of the globe, is no less impressive. Places of interest nearby include National Trust houses and gardens, Staverton Steam Railway, Paignton Zoo and Dartington Hall. **Directions:** Take A38 from Exeter or Plymouth, at Buckfastleigh take the A384 road for two miles. Turn left to Staverton. At Sea Trout Inn, take the left fork to Kingston and follow the signs.

Cottage Name	Sleeps	Bedrooms	Shower	Bath
THE OLD STABLES	4	2	1	1
BASS COURT	6	3	2	2

A member of
Premier Cottages Direct

TETBURY

PRICES

Smallest Cottage

from £200 to £450 per week

Largest Cottage

from £430 to £1040 per week

OTHER FACILITIES

Scenic views

Cot available

Shop nearby

Parking facilities

Garden furniture

Barbecue

Bicycle Hire

FOLLY FARM COTTAGES

TETBURY, GLOUCESTERSHIRE GL8 8XA
TEL: 01666 502475 FAX: 01666 502358 E-MAIL: info@gtb.co.uk
OWNERS: Jenni and Julian Benton

Buried deep in the serene isolation of the Cotswolds, the Folly Farm Cottages are one of Gloucestershire's, if not England's, best kept secrets. Set amidst 200 acres of lilting countryside estate these grade II listed cottages have been tastefully restored and now radiate a level of luxury one would expect of an estate dating back to the fifteenth century. The Great Tythe Barn is the focal point of this imperious rural hideaway. Combining traditional character with modern convenience it is ideal both for weddings and conferences alike. Soothingly lit, it is comprised of four main rooms simply steeped in history. Perhaps the most striking of the rooms is the Estcourt Gallery, a banqueting hall overlooked by a balustraded minstrel's gallery. It is here that sumptuous meals are served by relaxed, yet exacting staff. The wine and champagne list, wide-ranging and epitomising good taste, is guaranteed to appeal to even the most refined palate. The cottages themselves offer every modern comfort yet retain many of their original features such as log stoves and timber beamed roofs. The surrounding area is bathed in history and Folly Farm is situated in the renowned Royal Triangle. Highgrove, Gatcombe Park, Lypiatt Manor and Badminton are all within a short drive, as is the Westonbirt Arbitoreum. The beautiful cities of Cheltenham, Bath and Bristol are nearby. The region is ideal for lovers of golf, fishing and water sports. **Directions:** Leave M5 at junction 13 taking A419 to Stroud and follow the signs to Tetbury. Leave M4 at junction 17, bypass Malmesbury and then take B4014 to Tetbury.

Cottage Name	Sleeps	Bedrooms	Shower	Bath
MALTINGS	8	4	4	
WEIGH HOUSE	4	2	1	1
KILN	2	1	1	1

TEWKESBURY (Kemerton)

UPPER COURT COURTYARD COTTAGES

KEMERTON, NR TEWKESBURY, GLOUCESTERSHIRE GL20 7HY
TEL: 01386 725351 FAX: 01386 725472 E-MAIL: uppercourt@compuserve.com
OWNERS: Bill and Diana Herford

Situated in 15 acres of magnificent garden and grounds in one of the prettiest villages on Bredon Hill. Upper Court is an outstanding Cotswold manor circa 1760 with a large and impressive archway leading to a flower filled courtyard and a group of attractive holiday cottages, having every home comfort. They sleep from two to eight comfortably and are furnished in traditional country house-style with lovely antiques, chintzes and linens. Many have beamed ceilings or draped four-poster beds. Should visitors tire of catering for themselves excellent home-cooked meals can be delivered to their cottage and private dinner parties can be arranged in the Manor House. Excellent fresh English cooking is served at the Crown Inn, a short walk up the lane. The main feature of The National Garden Scheme garden is the lake, a two acre haven for a variety of wildfowl. A boat is available for rowing around the lake's two islands or for taking on a picnic. A heated outdoor swimming pool is in use from May until the end of August and there is an all-weather tennis court and a games room. Upper Court is an ideal base for visiting Tewkesbury and its abbey, Sudeley and Warwick castles, Gloucester, Worcester and Stratford. Bourton-on-the-Water and the Cotswold Wildlife Park at Burford will especially appeal to children. Bath and Hay-on-Wye for antiques and books. Short breaks are available. **Directions:** From Cheltenham 7 miles, travel north on the A435/B4079 and Kemerton is signed on the right just after the A46 crossroads.

PRICES

Smallest Cottage

from £280 to £488 per week

Largest Cottage

from £530 to £945 per week

OTHER FACILITIES

Scenic views

Cot available

Shop nearby

Parking facilities

Open Fire

Prepared meals available

Maid Service

Garden furniture

Barbecue

Cottage Name	Sleeps	Bedrooms	Shower	Bath
THE COURTYARD COTTAGE	8	3	1	1
THE STABLES	4/5	2	1	1
THE GALLERY	2	1	1	1
THE COACH HOUSE	6	3	1	1

OLD BRIDWELL HOLIDAY COTTAGES

BRIDWELL AVENUE, UFFCULME, DEVON EX15 3BU
TEL: 01884 841464 FAX: 01884 841474 E-MAIL: oldbridwell@eclipse.co.uk
OWNERS: Von Essen Hotels

Originally the homes of workers on the extensive Bridwell Park estate, these delightful and pretty cottages have been sympathetically restored to provide spacious and luxurious holiday accommodation in an idyllic country setting. Overlooking an attractive courtyard whose central feature is an old thatched pump-house, Thatched Cottage and adjoining Thatched Gables have been individually styled to offer the best of modern living whilst retaining all their original charm. From fully fitted kitchens to splendid bathrooms, each cottage provides a most relaxing and comfortable stay. They are centrally heated and equipped to the highest standards, including the provision of amenities such as electric oven, gas hob, fridge, freezer, washer/dryer, coffee maker, glassware, full table settings for 12 guests, colour television and security access system. There are other cottages which have not been inspected by Johansens. Garaging can be provided. Visitors can relax in and explore the colourful landscaped grounds, which include the original walled fruit garden. Alternatively, when feeling a little more energetic, they can seek out and enjoy the wild beauty of Exmoor and Dartmoor National Parks, the Blackdown Hills and the North Devon Coast. Cheddar Gorge, Wookey Holes and the clean safe beaches of Lyme Regis, Seaton, Branscombe, Salterton and Sidmouth are just a short drive away. Other cottages and out-of-season short breaks are available. **Directions:** Exit M5 at junction 27 onto the A38 towards Wellington. After ½ mile turn right towards Willand and then take the second turning on the left signed Uffculme and Working Wool Museum. Old Bridwell is on the left just past the main gates to Bridwell Park.

Cottage Name	Sleeps	Bedrooms	Shower	Bath
THATCHED COTTAGE	8	3		2
THATCHED GABLES	9	3	1	2

PRICES

Cottage
from £768
to £1817
per week

OTHER FACILITIES

Scenic views

Cot available

Shop nearby

Parking facilities

Open Fire

Laundry Service

Garden furniture

Barbecue

THE PRIORY

C/O RURAL RETREATS
TEL: 01386 701177 FAX: 01386 701178
OWNERS: Mr and Mrs A Willis

Dating back to the 16th century, The Priory is a wonderfully maintained imposing red-brick Tudor house. Grade II listed, it is the second oldest building in the hamlet of Wiggenhall St Mary Magdalen. The location is perhaps The Priory's most endearing feature. Surrounded by beautiful gardens, with the River Ouse to the rear, an air of calmness and seclusion prevails. The seven acres of garden offer stunning views of open countryside and walks along the riverbank. Masterfully blending tradition with modern convenience, The Priory has been tastefully renovated to its former splendour. The furnishings are extremely comfortable and elegant. The sitting room and dining room have charming inglenook fireplaces and thick wood beams. The stylish farmhouse kitchen is very well-equipped and overlooks the paddocks.

The spacious master bedroom, with its carved oak four-poster bed, is the height of luxury. Minutes away from Kings Lynn, The Priory provides a springboard for an exploration of North West Norfolk. Those with a penchant for walking will enjoy the location of the house and the picturesque bankside walks. The Sandringham Estate is a short drive to the west, with Kings Lynn only minutes away. Ely, with its imposing cathedral and profusion of teashops, is also close at hand. Visitors will also want to visit the beautiful colleges of Cambridge, with its vibrant nightlife and brilliant restaurants. Minimum stay 3 nights. Price on application. **Directions:** The Priory is in Wiggenhall St Mary Magdalen, a village just south of Kings Lynn, accessible via the A10.

Cottage Name	Sleeps	Bedrooms	Shower	Bath
THE PRIORY	8	4	4	4

WIVETON HALL

HOLT, NORFOLK NR25 7TE
TEL: 01263 740525 FAX: 01263 741314
OWNER: Desmond MacCarthy

This is the place for all those wanting to have a holiday break in peaceful historic style. The grand surrounds feature beams, open log fires, antique furnishings, polished wood floors, fine fabrics, oil paintings and prints alongside every modern amenity. Wiveton Hall, with its attractive lead paned windows and tall, patterned chimneys, is a lesser known architectural gem offering tranquil seclusion and magnificent panoramic views over the Norfolk marshes to the sea. It was built by a Jacobean merchant in the mid 17th century on monastic land close to the then thriving ports of Blakeney and Cley. A wing was added in 1908 to provide a ballroom, billiard room and gun room. This has now been converted into elegant, self contained, four-bedroom accommodation for up to eight visitors and has its own entrances and a courtyard garden. The ground floor ballroom is now a large, tastefully decorated drawing room with the additional luxury of a magnificent open fireplace and a grand piano and the billiard room is today's family-size kitchen/dining room. It is equipped to a high standard and has a wood burning stove. A utility room with dishwasher and washing machine opens onto the courtyard. Extensive gardens and farmland completely surround the Hall and guests are welcome to visit the working farm. Fly fishing for trout is available on a private lake on the property. Nearby are several long distance footpaths worth exploring, the nature reserves of Cley and Blakeney Point and a variety of beaches. Sandringham and the halls of Blickling, Felbrigg, Holkham and Houghton are within easy reach.

Cottage Name	Sleeps	Bedrooms	Shower	Bath
SELF CONTAINED WING	8	4		2

TALISKER.
A PLACE WHERE THE THUNDER ROLLS OVER YOUR TONGUE.

Of all the islands that defend Scotland's west coast from the Atlantic, Skye is the most dramatic. How fitting then that this is the home of the fiery Talisker. Standing on Skye's western shore, the distillery lies in the shadow of The Cuillins. Jagged mountains that rise out of the sea to skewer the clouds for a thunderous retort. In the shadow of these peaks, next to a fearsome sea, Talisker takes its first breath and draws it all in. Skye's explosive fervour captured forever in its only single malt. That Talisker is not a whisky for the faint-hearted is beyond dispute. Indeed even when one seasoned whisky taster once went as far as calling it "The lava of The Cuillins", no one disagreed.

Scotland

Myths and mountains, lochs and legends – Scotland's scenic splendour acts as a magnet for visitors from all over the globe. Superb as it is, Scotland's charismatic charm is more than just visual.

Dunrobin Castle

What's new in Scotland?

• The Big Idea – aiming to be open in the spring of 2000, a state-of-the-art permanent exhibition will be launched on the west coast of Scotland on the Ardeer peninsula. This is a visitor experience, not a science museum, nor an exploratorium but a gigantic workshop where visitors are encouraged to have their own big ideas.

•Scottish Seabird Centre – expected to open in May 2000 in North Berwick, offers visitors an amazing insight into the some of the largest seabird colonies in Europe.

•Our Dynamic Earth – this new visitor attraction opened in July 1999 directly opposite the site of the new Scottish parliament and close to the Palace of Holyroodhouse and tells the story of our planet. Using dramatic special effects this attraction takes the visitor through the fascinating journey from the Earth's creation through to the future (whatever it may be!) Travel through time and step aboard a spaceship and see the creation of earth and the splendour of the natural world.

For further information, please contact:-

The Scottish Tourist Board
23 Ravelston Terrace
Edinburgh
EH4 3TP

Tel: 0131 332 2433

FOREST HILLS

KINLOCHARD BY ABERFOYLE, THE TROSSACHS FK8 3TL
TEL: 01877 387277 FAX: 01877 387307
OWNERS: Macdonald Hotels

The majestic and rambling Forest Hills is delightfully enveloped in 25 acres of gardens and woodlands overlooking beautiful Loch Ard in the foothills of the Trossachs, scattered with tumbling burns, rocky waterfalls, winding pathways and meandering forest trails. It is a stunning, history-steeped scenic area where hotel guests can unwind and immerse themselves in the surrounding landscape. The very highest standards of accommodation may be enjoyed by those staying in one of the excellent self-catering apartments. Sleeping from four to eight people, these opulent properties are ideal for families wishing to relax in style whilst enjoying the comforts of home. Each apartment is bedecked with attractive furnishings and soft fabrics, creating a most relaxing atmosphere. A wide array of modern facilities complements the stylish interior. The fully fitted kitchen has been designed with a self-catering break in mind whilst those seeking a break from the kitchen may dine at the hotel's New Rafters Bar and Bistro where grills, pasta and salads may be enjoyed. The hotel's leisure centre will appeal to the more active visitor as its facilities include a heated swimming pool, gymnasium, billiards and a curling rink which converts into an extensive children's play area with go-karts. Those with a penchant for water sports can enjoy canoeing, windsurfing and sailing on the Loch. **Directions:** From the M9, exit at junction 10. Take the A873 to Aberfoyle and then join the B829 to Kinlochard. The road winds by the lochside along to Forest Hills. The nearest train station is Stirling.

Cottage Name	Sleeps	Bedrooms	Shower	Bath
ROWAN	6	2	1	2
OAK	6	2	1	2
SPRUCE	6/8	3	1	2
RED MAPLE	6	2	1	2
SILVER BIRCH	6	2	1	2
LOCH SIDE	6	2	1	2

MAR LODGE

MAR LODGE ESTATE, BRAEMAR, ABERDEENSHIRE AB35 5YJ
TEL: 0131 243 9331 FAX: 0131 243 9589 E-MAIL: holidays@nts.org.uk
OWNER: The National Trust for Scotland

Mar Lodge is something special, standing regally in the heart of a 77,500 acre estate that is part of the core area of the Cairngorm Mountains, recognised as the most important nature conservation landscape in Britain. Wildlife and birdlife abound, the scenery is spectacular and the air is clean and fresh. The estate contains four of the highest mountains in the country and also includes the upper watershed of the River Dee and the remnants of an ancient Caledonian pine forest. Queen Victoria laid the foundation stone of Mar Lodge in 1895. It was built for her granddaughter, Princess Louise, who had married the Duke of Fife and it remained in the Duke's family until 1962. The National Trust of Scotland acquired the Lodge in 1995 and it has now been converted into luxurious apartments sleeping from two to 15 guests. The largest, Bynack, is on two levels, has seven bedrooms and is entered through the front door of the house. All apartments are furnished to the highest standards using, where appropriate, furniture original to the building. They are centrally heated, have television, payphone and kitchens incorporating every modern amenity. Guests can also use the ground floor dining room, drawing room and library of the Lodge. There are other cottages on the estate which have not been inspected by Johansens. Shooting, stalking, fishing, climbing, walking and skiing are popular leisure pursuits. Nearby is Braemar, 1,100 feet above sea level and famous for September Highland Gathering, Balmoral and a wealth of other Royal Deeside attractions. **Directions:** Turn off the A93 into Braemar and follow the signs to Linn of Dee. Mar Lodge is on the right, 6 miles from the village.

Cottage Name	Sleeps	Bedrooms	Shower	Bath
BYNACK	15	7	4	4
DERRY	4	2	1	1
BRAERIACH	2/3	1	1	1

PRICES

Smallest Cottage
from £385
to £575
per week

Largest Cottage
from £500
to £900
per week

OTHER FACILITIES

Scenic views

Cot available

Parking facilities

Open Fire

Maid Service

Garden furniture

Barbecue

KINNAIRD ESTATE

BY DUNKELD, PERTHSHIRE PH8 0LB
TEL: 01796 482440 FAX: 01796 482289
OWNER: Mrs Constance Ward

Offering breathtaking views across the moors and the Tay Valley, Kinnaird is surrounded by a captivating estate of 9,000 acres and is tailor made for aficionados of outdoor sports and those seeking a relaxing break. Built in 1770 the house was completely renovated in 1990 by Constance Ward. Visitors to the cottages may avail of the main hotel's stylishly decorated dining room where delicious fare is served in a relaxing ambience. The cottages are simply exquisite. Castle Peroch, as its name suggests, is set high above Kinnaird House, offering views that linger long in the memory. An ideal hideaway in both summer and winter, its spacious L-shaped living room is dominated by a vast open fireplace, while the patio and adjoining kitchen are a suntrap during the warmer months. With panoramic vistas over the Tay Valley, Keepers Cottage is part of the original stables. Both the sitting room and kitchen benefit from open log fires. One of the largest cottages with four bedrooms, Balnamuir Farm House is much in demand from families and shooting and hunting parties. Glorious views of the Scottish highlands are also enjoyed from here. Those in search of seclusion should look no further than Ferry Cottage, a riverside retreat surrounded by dense woods sleeping a maximum of four. Pheasant , situated in the charming hamlet of Kincraigie is well appointed and is ideal for a young family. There are other cottages on the estate, please ask for details. A wide range of sporting facilities is available from salmon and trout fishing to bird-watching and pheasant watching. **Directions:** Two miles north of Dunkeld on the A9, take B898 for 4½ miles.

Cottage Name	Sleeps	Bedrooms	Shower	Bath
PHEASANT COTTAGE	4/6	3		1
CASTLE PEROCH	4	2	1	1
FERRY COTTAGE	4	2		1
BALNAMUIR FARM HOUSE	8	4	2	2
KEEPER COTTAGE	4	2		2

PRICES

Smallest Cottage
from £200
to £335
per week

Largest Cottage
from £400
to £620
per week

OTHER FACILITIES

Scenic views

Cot available

Parking facilities

Maid Service

Garden furniture

Barbecue

Children's Play Area

THE OLD STEADING

CARDEN, ALVES, ELGIN, MORAY IV30 8UP
TEL: 01343 850222 FAX: 01343 850626 E-MAIL: carden@enterprise.net
OWNERS: Gavin and Suzanne MacKessack-Leitch

The Old Steading offers peaceful, historic countryside sprinkled with ancient castles and fortresses, golf courses, country pursuit centres and magnificent sandy beaches within a 20 minutes drive away. It is a delightful, relaxing atmosphere in which to enjoy a well earned break. The cottages, renovated from the original farm Steading buildings, surround an attractive, south facing courtyard. Each has been individually designed to take advantage of the setting and views over open farmland to the distant northern hills. The owners have retained many of the cottages original features which comfortably combine with all modern facilities. Each has central heating and double glazing, kitchens are extensively fitted out with electric and microwave cookers, fridge/freezer, washing machine and tumble drier. The spacious living room and bedrooms are tastefully decorated with co-ordinating soft furnishings, there is remote control television with teletext and video recorder and each cottage has a private patio garden. Visitors can enjoy the use of an all-weather tennis court and a well equipped games room. Children will be pleased with the on-site play area and a farm walk. During the summer months the beaches and fishing villages of the Moray Coast are a great attraction, as are 'explorations' of the numerous distilleries and whisky trails around the Rivers Spey and Findhorn. Elgin, with its ruined 13th century cathedral is just a short drive away, as is the bustling resort of Lossiemouth, 13th century Pluscarden Abbey and 14th century Balvenie Castle. **Directions:** The Old Steading is 4 miles west of Elgin, just off A96 Aberdeen to Inverness Road.

Cottage Name	Sleeps	Bedrooms	Shower	Bath
THE MILL HOUSE	4	2	1	1
THE BARN	6	3	2	1
THE BOTHY	2	1	1	1

HELMSDALE (Sutherland)

NAVIDALE LODGES

NAVIDALE HOUSE HOTEL, HELMSDALE, SUTHERLAND KW8 6JS
TEL: 01431 821258 FAX: 01431 821531
OWNERS: Navidale House Ltd

Newly built to exceptionally high standards, The Navidale Lodges lie within the private woodlands and wonderfully maintained gardens of the Navidale House Hotel. Commanding stunning views of the Moray Forth, visitors have found peace and seclusion beyond compare. In more convivial moments guests can take refuge in the bar and restaurant of the fabulous hotel. The restaurant, with its international cuisine tenderly crafted from the freshest of local produce, is suffused with a lively and open atmosphere. Specialities include fish and seafood, Caithness beef and local venison. The cottages themselves are gorgeously appointed and contain every modern convenience, with modishly designed bathrooms and furnishings. The renowned Helmsdale and Brora rivers, awash with salmon and sea trout, are complemented by the Helmsdale Locks, famous for their abundance of wild brown trout. Stalking, wild-fowling and shooting on wind-swept country estates can also be arranged. For golf lovers, there is the magnificent Royal Dornoch, an 18 hole championship links with five other 18 hole courses in the vicinity. Ornithologists will delight in the superfluity of birdlife at Forsinard, an RSPB reserve. On local cliffs visitors can view puffins while inland ospreys and golden eagles can be observed. In nearby Helmsdale, the Timespan Centre gives a unique insight into history of the local settlements and other Highland Clearances. At Clynelish distillery one can observe the production of Scotland's most famous export. **Directions:** Situated half a mile north of Helmsdale, just off the A9 coastal road.

Cottage Name	Sleeps	Bedrooms	Shower	Bath
SOUTH LODGE 1	6	3	1	1
SOUTH LODGE 2	5	3	1	1

PRICES

Cottage
from £379
to £577
per week

OTHER FACILITIES

Scenic views

Cot available

Parking facilities

Open Fire

Prepared meals available

Garden furniture

Barbecue

Bicycle Hire

ACHNEIM COTTAGE

CAWDOR ESTATE, NAIRN, NR INVERNESS
ENQUIRIES, CONTACT RURAL RETREATS
TEL: 01386 701177 FAX: 01386 701178 E-MAIL: info@ruralretreats.co.uk

Tucked away among the peaceful countryside just south of the Moray Firth between Inverness and Nairn is a small, solidly built refurbished and redecorated gamekeeper's lodge that offers a total tranquil retreat. Just two miles from Cawdor the cottage stands secluded off a quiet country lane providing occupants with superb panoramic views over to the sea from its small paned sash windows. It is cosy and warm with central heating throughout and a welcoming open fire to curl up in front of in the large sitting room. Achneim sleeps two and is fully equipped with all home comforts. A bath/shower room complements the tastefully decorated and furnished double bedroom and kitchen facilities include a dishwasher, microwave cooker, washing machine and tumble drier. Maid and baby sitting services, fishing, riding, clay and rifle shooting can be arranged and those

with a penchant for walking may explore the Drynachan Valley and the River Findhorn. Between May and October, visitors to the cottage receive two complimentary tickets to nearby Cawdor Castle and its magnificent grounds. There are many other castles in the area as well as numerous distilleries to visit. Also popular is the market town of Elgin with its ruined 13th century cathedral, the resort of Nairn with its fine sands, fishing and golf, 13th century Pluscarden Priory and Culloden Battlefield. Minimum stay 3 nights. Price on application.
Directions: From Inverness, take the A96 towards Nairn. After approximately 8 miles turn right onto the B9090 for Cawdor. At the Village Hall crossroads turn right. Turn right again at the small crossroads after the castle entrance. After about ½ mile turn left up a lane opposite farm buildings. Achneim Cottage is 50m ahead.

Cottage Name	Sleeps	Bedrooms	Shower	Bath
ACHNEIM COTTAGE	2	1	1	1

BLAIRMORE

GLASS, BY HUNTLY, ABERDEENSHIRE AB54 4XH
TEL: 01466 700200 FAX: 01466 700205
CONTACTS: Monique and Hans Baumann

Blairmore House is an imposing 19th century country mansion at the heart of a 40-acre estate in the beautiful Deveron Valley, surrounded by wooded hills and pine forests, salmon rivers and streams flowing beside quiet roads climbing high into the Grampians. It is known as Scotland's 'Castle Country' because there are more than 70 castles to visit and enjoy, as well as eight of the most famous malt whisky distilleries. The luxurious, beautifully decorated and furnished nine bedroom mansion is let only on an all inclusive basis but there are delightful, stone built, self catering holiday cottages on the estate that offer a peaceful and comfortable rural retreat from town and city life. Each is furnished and equipped to the highest standard. Apple Cottage, detached and single storey, stands in a secluded position next to the walled garden in wooded grounds. It sleeps three in a double and single bedroom, has a well equipped kitchen and an open fire in the sitting/dining room. Traditional Holly Tree Cottage has its own private garden in which to relax and breathe in the freshest of air while listening to the tinkling waters of a little stream flowing past your garden chair. Sleeping five this superb cottage has recently been restored and refurbished to feature an open-plan kitchen with breakfast bar, sitting room with open fire and an elegant dining room. There are other cottages on the estate which have not been inspected by Johansens. Superb walks have been created through the estate and local forest, there are several golf courses in the area and fishing, stalking, pheasant, grouse and duck shoots can be arranged. **Directions:** From Huntley take the A920 Dufftown Road and turn left at the sign Blairmore School and Glass Church.

Cottage Name	Sleeps	Bedrooms	Shower	Bath
BLAIRMORE HOUSE	18	9	9	8
HOLLY TREE COTTAGE	5	3	2	1
APPLE COTTAGE	3	2	1	1

PRICES

Smallest Cottage

from £190
to £425
per week

Largest Cottage

from £275
to £525
per week

OTHER FACILITIES

Scenic views

Cot available

Parking facilities

Open Fire

Maid Service

Garden furniture

Barbecue

DUNTULM COASTGUARD COTTAGES

DUNTULM, TROTTERNISH, ISLE OF SKYE IV51 9UF
TEL: 01470 552213 FAX: 01470 552292
OWNERS: Andrew and Pamela Butler

These sparkling white, adjoining coastguard cottages are situated in a peaceful and dramatic location on the Trotternish peninsula with superb sea views across the broad waters of the Minch to the Outer Isles, spectacular sunsets and fascinating dancing displays of the Northern Lights. Standing within 400 yards of the shore they are bursting with nautical character. Traditionally and solidly built as a coastguard station in 1933 they have been restored, renovated and furnished to award-winning standards and offer a cosy stay, even on the coldest winter day. Each cottage is fitted with every modern facility and amenity, including being fully double glazed. As well as central heating there is an open fire in the lounge with an ample supply of coal and logs supplied. The cottages are quiet and secluded. The rear overlooks picturesque Loch Cleat, which offers excellent fishing, at the front there is a lawned garden with picnic bench, a relaxing spot for a summer evening's barbecue. The cottages are let separately, but together can provide accommodation for special interest groups for up to 24 people. Walkers exploring the unspoilt coastline will enjoy coming across the many cairns, standing stones and an occasional historic ruin. Uig Pier and Flora MacDonald's Monument are worth a visit. Golf can be played at nearby Skeabost and pony trekking, sea canoeing, windsurfing and cycle hire can be arranged. **Directions:** From Portree, take the A855 Staffin Road for approximately 22 miles. From Uig, the cottages are 8 miles on the Staffin Road.

Cottage Name	Sleeps	Bedrooms	Shower	Bath
HUNISH	8/10	4		1
MEANISH	6/7	3		1
ERISCO	6/7	3		1

PRICES

Smallest Cottage

from £250
to £350
per week

Largest Cottage

from £450
to £850
per week

OTHER FACILITIES

Scenic views

Parking facilities

Open Fire

Laundry Service

Garden furniture

Bicycle Hire

STUCAN-T-IOBAIRT COTTAGE

TARBET, ARROCHAR, LOCH LOMOND, SCOTLAND G83 7DL
TEL/FAX: 0141 339 2774 E-MAIL: cottage@colemanscottage.force9.co.uk
OWNER: Ian Coleman

On the shores overlooking Loch Lomond, this tranquil retreat affords breathtaking views of the surrounding Scottish landscape. The attractive 370 year old cottage is enveloped in beautifully maintained grounds comprising lawns, a little burn and a river. Historians will be delighted with the impressive yew tree which dates back over a thousand years and was reputedly the spot where Robert the Bruce assembled his troops. The accommodation consists of a large cottage sleeping 4 to 6 and a second for two people. Guests may either have exclusive use of the two properties or rent a single cottage depending on the season. The rooms are heated and adorned with attractive tartan or country drapes and linen. There are a number of facilities to please today's modern traveller such as satellite television, a dishwasher, payphone and a maid service is available. The well-appointed kitchen features artfully concealed equipment and is enhanced by a wood burning stove. Throughout the property, old beams and roaring log fires add to the charm and character of this inviting retreat. There are a number of restaurants and small inns within the vicinity and the attentive staff will be pleased to recommend those suitable for fine dining. This idyllic location will appeal to wildlife enthusiasts as deer, goats and eagles may be seen. The more adventurous may try their hand at fishing, golfing, sailing, hill-climbing or exploring one of the nearby lochs. The cultural city of Glasgow with its plethora of art galleries and museums is only an hour away. **Directions:** M74 to Glasgow, follow M8 Glasgow North, follow signs for and past Glasgow Airport to Erskin Bridge turn off, cross bridge (60p toll). Follow Crianlarich signs onto A82, stay on this road past Luss exit, Inverbeg Inn Hotel, all the way to the cottage.

Cottage Name	Sleeps	Bedrooms	Shower	Bath
STUCAN-T-IOBAIRT COTTAGE	4/6	3	2	2
GARDEN COTTAGE	2	1	1	

PRICES

Cottage
from £250
to £495
per week
+ VAT

OTHER FACILITIES

Scenic views

Parking facilities

Open Fire

Garden furniture

CAMUSERICHT ESTATE

BRIDGE OF GAUR, RANNOCH, PERTHSHIRE PH17 2QP
TEL: 01882 633207 FAX: 01882 633273
HOSTS: Sue and Leigh Kerfoot

Set at the mouth of the river Ericht and with captivating views of Loch Rannoch, Camusericht is a traditional highland sporting estate. Surrounded by 12,000 acres of highland Perthshire, with the imperious Schiehallon at the eastern end of the loch, Camusericht is ideal for walkers, bird-watchers and sports lovers alike. Anglers will not want to miss some of the best freshwater fishing in the British Isles, and the estate has rights on numerous lochs in the vicinity as well as the River Gaur. A mile from the Lodge, but still on the estate, Tigh na Vilt is a fully refurbished gamekeepers cottage set in its own two acre garden. Bright and breezy, it is appointed in a non-traditional but warm and cosy style. There are many places of interest within the locality including numerous golf courses. While on the loch, visitors can indulge their passions for wind-surfing and sailing, and for the more adventurous there is nearby white water rafting. Whisky distilleries and historic castles, such as Blair and Castle Menzies, are dotted around the region. Camusericht Lodge itself, with its original pine staircase and walls covered in family portraits and hunting trophies, is occasionally let to large parties on a fully catered and staffed basis. Details on application. Adjacent to the Lodge is a large indoor heated swimming pool and gymnasium complex complete with turreted staircase, which is sometimes available for guests in Tigh na Vilt, but usually retained for the exclusive use of guests in the Lodge. **Directions:** Take the A9 north to Calvine. Turn left, then immediately right onto the B847. Follow the signposts to Kinloch Rannoch. Tigh na Vilt is 10 miles along the north shore.

Cottage Name	Sleeps	Bedrooms	Shower	Bath
TIGH NA VILT	5	3	1	1

PRICES

Smallest Cottage
from £350 to £525 per week

Largest Cottage
from £700 to £1200 per week

OTHER FACILITIES

Scenic views

Cot available

Shop nearby

Parking facilities

Open Fire

Garden furniture

Barbecue

BURNKNOWE HOUSE & COTTAGE

INVERLOANIN ROAD, LOCHGOILHEAD, SCOTLAND
TEL: 01555 893592 FAX: 01555 894919
OWNERS: Andrew Brown

This is a venue of complete relaxation and tranquillity projected magnificently from one of Scotland's most beautiful hillside settings. Burnknowe rises high and impressively over Loch Goil. Its cream and white exterior contrasts starkly with the surrounding and rising deep green woodlands whilst its terraced gardens slope gradually and grandly down to the loch's deep tidal sea waters. Burnknowe is without doubt a dramatic Victorian delight with stunning views and a comforting ambience that has to be experienced to be believed. Whether taking in the panoramic views from the 11 window tower observatory, enjoying the colourful sights and sounds of the extensive lawned, flower-bedded and shrub-filled gardens with tinkling waterfall, planning your next woodland walk for wildlife spotting, or simply curling up in front of comforting log fires this can be the holiday of

your dreams. Visitors have the use of a shoreline summer house, boathouse, private jetty, canoes and clinker style boats. Life jackets are available. Four bedrooms with all home-from-home comforts accommodate eight guests. A sunny breakfast room helps throw off a good night's sleep and there is an elegant sitting room and a fitted kitchen to suit the most discerning cook. Lochgoilhead village with its small shopping facilities is a 15 minutes walk away and the scenic West Coast of Scotland, the Mull of Kintyre and Glasgow are within easy reach. **Directions:** From Glasgow, take A82 north and at Tarbet turn left onto A83 west. After approx.7 miles turn left onto B828 to Lochgoilhead. Burnknowe Cottage is adjacent, but outwith the grounds of the house. When renting the cottage separately from the house there is no access to the shore, jetty, boathouse etc.

Cottage Name	Sleeps	Bedrooms	Shower	Bath
BURNKNOWE HOUSE	8	4	1	1
BURNKNOWE COTTAGE	4	2	1	1

PRICES

Smallest Cottage
from £300
to £500
per week

COBWEBS

40 NORTH STREET, ST ANDREWS, FIFE KY16 9AH
TEL: 01334 650000 or 0870 474414 E-MAIL: enquiries@cobwebs.co.uk
OWNER: F Robertson

OTHER FACILITIES

Cot available

Shop nearby

Parking facilities

Laundry Service

Maid Service

Garden furniture

Barbecue

This attractive, compact apartment is conveniently situated in the heart of historical St Andrews overlooking the town's early 15th century university, predated in Britain only by Oxford and Cambridge. The internationally famous championship golf course, 15th century castle and ruined splendour of a 15th century cathedral are just a few minutes walk away. Cobwebs is an ideal base for a family wishing to soak up the history and culture of a medieval town that has a unique place in Scotland's heritage while at the same time enjoying its modern delights and surprises. The apartment is part of an 18th century listed building and is entered by a wrought-iron framed staircase which leads onto a small, sun catching patio that is furnished with relaxing chairs and table. The lawned garden faces south and is enhanced with colourful flower beds and fruit trees. Due to the building's age the rooms in the apartment appear fairly small, but they are delightfully decorated and furnished and have every home-from-home comfort. A double, twin and single bedroom are on the first floor with an attractive sitting room on the second floor offering views over the walled garden. Meals are taken at the breakfast bar in the adjoining, fully-equipped kitchen which has an electric cooker, microwave oven, fridge, dishwasher and telephone for incoming calls. An automatic washing machine and tumble dryer are located in a laundry room. Maid service is available and baby equipment in addition to a provided cot and high chair can be arranged. There are numerous excellent restaurants and cafes nearby. **Directions:** From the M90, exit at junction 8 and take the A91 east to St Andrews.

Cottage Name	Sleeps	Bedrooms	Shower	Bath
COBWEBS	5	3	1	1

Johansens Recommended Hotels Great Britain & Ireland

ENGLAND

Abberley (Worcester) – The Elms, Abberley, Worcestershire WR6 6AT. Tel: 01299 896666

Acton Trussell (Stafford) – The Moat House, Acton Trussell, Stafford, Staffordshire ST17 0RJ. Tel: 01785 712217

Aldeburgh – Wentworth Hotel, Wentworth Road, Aldeburgh, Suffolk IP15 5BD. Tel: 01728 452312

Alderley Edge – The Alderley Edge Hotel, Macclesfield Road, Alderley Edge, Cheshire SK9 7BJ. Tel: 01625 583033

Alfriston – White Lodge Country House Hotel, Sloe Lane, Alfriston, East Sussex BN26 5UR. Tel: 01323 870265

Alston – Lovelady Shield Country House Hotel, Nenthead Road, Alston, Cumbria CA9 3LF. Tel: 01434 381203

Altrincham – Woodland Park Hotel, Wellington Road, Timperley, Altrincham, Cheshire WA15 7RG. Tel: 0161 928 8631

Ambleside – Holbeck Ghyll Country House Hotel & Health Spa, Holbeck Lane, Windermere , Cumbria LA23 1LU. Tel: 015394 32375

Ambleside – Rothay Manor, Rothay Bridge, Ambleside, Cumbria LA22 0EH. Tel: 015394 33605

Ambleside (Clappersgate) – Nanny Brow Country House Hotel & Restaurant, Clappersgate, Ambleside, Cumbria LA22 9NF. Tel: 015394 32036

Ambleside (Great Langdale) – Langdale Hotel & Country Club, Great Langdale, Nr Ambleside, Cumbria LA22 9JD. Tel: 015394 37302

Andover (Hurstborne Tarrant) – Esseborne Manor, Hurstborne Tarrant, Andover, Hampshire SP11 0ER. Tel: 01264 736444

Andover (Middle Wallop) – Fifehead Manor, Middle Wallop, Stockbridge, Hampshire SO20 8EG. Tel: 01264 781565

Appleby-in-Westmorland – Appleby Manor Country House Hotel, Roman Road, Appleby-in-Westmorland, Cumbria CA16 6JB. Tel: 017683 51571

Appleby-In-Westmorland – Tufton Arms Hotel, Market Square, Appleby-In-Westmorland, Cumbria CA16 6XA. Tel: 017683 51593

Arundel (Climping) – Bailiffscourt, Climping, Nr Arundel, West Sussex BN17 5RW. Tel: 01903 723511

Ascot – Royal Berkshire, London Road, Sunninghill, Ascot, Berkshire SL5 0PP. Tel: 01344 623322

Ashbourne – Callow Hall, Mappleton Road, Ashbourne, Derbyshire DE6 2AA. Tel: 01335 343403

Ashbourne (Dovedale) – The Izaak Walton Hotel, Dovedale, Near Ashbourne, Derbyshire DE6 2AY. Tel: 01335 350555

Ashburton – Holne Chase Hotel & Restaurant, Nr Ashburton, Devon TQ13 7NS. Tel: 01364 631471

Ashford (Boughton Lees) – Eastwell Manor, Boughton Lees, Ashford, Kent TN25 4HR. Tel: 01233 213000

Ashford-In-The-Water – Riverside House, Ashford-In-The-Water, Nr Bakewell, Derbyshire DE45 1QF. Tel: 01629 814275

Axminster (Chardstock) – Tytherleigh Cot Hotel, Chardstock, Axminster, Devon EX13 7BN. Tel: 01460 221170

Aylesbury – Hartwell House, Oxford Road, Nr Aylesbury, Buckinghamshire HP17 8NL. Tel: 01296 747444

Aylesbury (Witchurch) – The Priory Hotel, High Street, Witchurch, Aylesbury, Buckinghamshire HP22 4JS. Tel: 01296 641239

Bagshot – Pennyhill Park Hotel And Country Club, London Road, Bagshot, Surrey GU19 5ET. Tel: 01276 471774

Bakewell – Hassop Hall, Hassop, Nr Bakewell, Derbyshire DE45 1NS. Tel: 01629 640488

Banbury (Wroxton St Mary) – Wroxton House Hotel, Wroxton St Mary, Banbury, Oxfordshire OX15 6QB. Tel: 01295 730777

Basingstoke (Rotherwick) – Tylney Hall, Rotherwick, Hook, Hampshire RG27 9AZ. Tel: 01256 764881

Baslow – The Cavendish Hotel, Baslow, Derbyshire DE4 1SP. Tel: 01246 582311

Baslow – Fischer's, Baslow Hall, Calver Road, Baslow, Derbyshire DE45 1RR. Tel: 01246 583259

Bath – The Bath Priory Hotel and Restaurant, Weston Road, Bath, Somerset BA1 2XT. Tel: 01225 331922

Bath – Combe Grove Manor & Country Club, Brassknocker Hill, Monkton Combe, Bath, Somerset BA2 7HS. Tel: 01225 834644

Bath – The Queensberry, Russel Street, Bath, Somerset BA1 2QF. Tel: 01225 447928

Bath – The Royal Crescent Hotel, Royal Crescent, Bath, Somerset BA1 2LS. Tel: 01225 823333

Bath (Colerne) – Lucknam Park, Colerne, Nr Bath, Wiltshire SN14 8AZ. Tel: 01225 742777

Bath (Hinton Charterhouse) – Homewood Park, Hinton Charterhouse, Bath, Somerset BA3 6BB. Tel: 01225 723731

Bath (Hunstrete) – Hunstrete House, Hunstrete, Pensford, Nr Bristol , Somerset BS39 4NS. Tel: 01761 490490

Bath (Ston Easton) – Ston Easton Park, Ston Easton, Bath, Somerset BA3 4DF. Tel: 01761 241631

Battle – Netherfield Place Hotel & Country Club, Netherfield Hill, Battle, East Sussex TN33 9PP. Tel: 01424 774455

Battle – PowderMills Hotel, Powdermill Lane, Battle, East Sussex TN33 0SP. Tel: 01424 775511

Beaminster – Bridge House Hotel, Beaminster, Dorset DT8 3AY. Tel: 01308 862200

Beaulieu – The Montagu Arms Hotel, Beaulieu, New Forest, Hampshire SO42 7ZL. Tel: 01590 612324

Beaulieu (Buckler's Hard) – The Master Builder's House, Buckler's Hard, Beaulieu, New Forest, Hampshire SO42 7XB. Tel: 01590 616253

Bedford (Clapham) – Woodlands Manor, Green Lane, Clapham, Bedford, Bedfordshire MK41 6EP. Tel: 01234 363281

Berwick-Upon-Tweed – Marshall Meadow Country House Hotel, Berwick-Upon-Tweed, Northumberland TD15 1UT. Tel: 01289 331133

Berwick-Upon-Tweed – Tillmouth Park, Cornhill-on-Tweed, Nr Berwick-Upon-Tweed, Northumberland TD12 4UU. Tel: 01890 882255

Bibury – The Swan Hotel At Bibury, Bibury, Gloucestershire GL7 5NW. Tel: 01285 740695

Birmingham – The Burlington Hotel, 6 Burlington Arcade, 126 New Street, Birmingham, West Midlands B2 4JQ. Tel: 0121 643 9191

Birmingham – The Swallow Hotel, 12, Hagley Road, Fiveways, Birmingham, West Midlands B16 8SJ. Tel: 0121 455 7073

Birmingham (King's Norton) – The Mill House Hotel & Lombard Room Restaurant, 180 Lifford Lane, King's Norton, Birmingham, West Midlands B30 3NT. Tel: 0121 459 5800

Birmingham (Walmley) – New Hall, Walmley Road, Royal Sutton Coldfield, West Midlands B76 1QX. Tel: 0121 378 2442

Bishop's Stortford (Hatfield Heath) – Down Hall Country House Hotel, Hatfield Heath, Nr Bishop's Stortford, Hertfordshire CM22 7AS. Tel: 01279 731441

Blackburn (Darwen) – Astley Bank Hotel & Conference Centre, Bolton Road, Darwen, Nr Blackburn, Lancashire. Tel: 01254 777700

Bolton Abbey (Skipton) – The Devonshire Arms Country House Hotel, Bolton Abbey, Skipton, North Yorkshire BD23 6AJ. Tel: 01756 710441

Bournemouth – Langtry Manor, Derby Road, East cliff, Bournemouth, Dorset BH1 3QB. Tel: 01202 553887

Bournemouth – The Norfolk Royale Hotel, Richmond Hill, Bournemouth, Dorset BH2 6EN. Tel: 01202 551521

Bournemouth (Ferndown) – The Dormy, New Road, Ferndown, Near Bournemouth, Dorset BH22 8ES. Tel: 01202 872121

Bovey Tracey – The Edgemoor, Haytor Road, Bovey Tracey, Devon TQ13 9LE. Tel: 01626 832466

Bradford-On-Avon – Woolley Grange, Woolley Green, Bradford-On-Avon, Wiltshire BA15 1TX. Tel: 01225 864705

Brampton – Farlam Hall Hotel, Brampton, Cumbria CA8 2NG. Tel: 016977 46234

Bray-on-Thames – Chauntry House Hotel & Restaurant, Bray-on-Thames, Berkshire SL6 2AB. Tel: 01628 673991

Bray-on-Thames – Monkey Island Hotel, Bray-on-Thames, Maidenhead, Berkshire SL6 2EE. Tel: 01628 623400

Brighton – The Old Ship Hotel, Kings Road, Brighton, East Sussex BN1 1NR. Tel: 01273 329001

Bristol – Hotel Du Vin & Bistro, The Sugar House, Narrow Lewins Mead, Bristol, BS1 2NU. Tel: 0117 925 5577

Bristol – Swallow Royal Hotel, College Green, Bristol BS1 5TA. Tel: 0117 9255100/200

Bristol South (Shipham) – Daneswood House Hotel, Cuck Hill, Shipham, Nr Winscombe, Somerset BS25 1RD. Tel: 01934 843145

Broadway – Dormy House, Willersey Hill, Broadway, Worcestershire WR12 7LF. Tel: 01386 852711

Broadway – The Lygon Arms, Broadway, Worcestershire WR12 7DU. Tel: 01386 852255

Brockenhurst – The Balmer Lawn, Lyndhurst Road, Brockenhurst, New Forest, Hampshire SO42 7ZB. Tel: 01590 623116

Brockenhurst – Careys Manor Hotel, Brockenhurst, New Forest, Hampshire SO42 7RH. Tel: 01590 623551

Brockenhurst – New Park Manor, Lyndhurst Road, Brockenhurst, New Forest, Hampshire SO42 7QH. Tel: 01590 623467

Brockenhurst – Rhinefield House Hotel, Rhinefield Road, Brockenhurst, Hampshire SO42 7QB. Tel: 01590 622922

Bromsgrove – Grafton Manor Country House Hotel, Grafton Lane, Bromsgrove, Worcestershire B61 7HA. Tel: 01527 579007

Burford – The Bay Tree Hotel & Restaurant, Sheep Street, Burford, Oxford OX18 4LW. Tel: 01993 822791

Burnham Market – The Hoste Arms Hotel, The Green, Burnham Market, Norfolk PE31 8HD. Tel: 01328 738777

Burrington (Nr Umberleigh) – Northcote Manor Country House Hotel, Burrington, Nr Umberleigh, Devon EX37 9LZ. Tel: 01769 560501

Bury St Edmunds – The Angel Hotel, Bury St Edmunds, Suffolk IP33 1LT. Tel: 01284 753926

Bury St Edmunds – Ravenwood Hall, Rougham, Bury St Edmunds, Suffolk IP30 9JA. Tel: 01359 270345

Buxted, Near Uckfield – Buxted Park Country House Hotel, Buxted, Uckfield, East Sussex TN22 4AY. Tel: 01825 732711

Buxton – The Lee Wood Hotel & Restaurant, The Park, Buxton, Derbyshire SK17 6TQ. Tel: 01298 23002

Buxton – The Palace Hotel, Palace Road, Buxton, Derbyshire SK17 6AG. Tel: 01298 22001

Canterbury (Chartham Hatch) – Howfield Manor, Chartham Hatch, Canterbury, Kent CT4 7HQ. Tel: 01227 738294

Castle Combe – The Manor House Hotel & Golf Club, Castle Combe, Chippenham, Wiltshire SN14 7HR. Tel: 01249 782206

Chaddesley Corbett (Nr Kidderminster) – Brockencote Hall, Chaddesley Corbett, Nr Kidderminster, Worcestershire DY10 4PY. Tel: 01562 777876

Chagford – Gidleigh Park, Chagford, Devon TQ13 8HH. Tel: 01647 432367

Chelmsford (Great Baddow) – Pontlands Park Country Hotel, West Hanningfield Road, Great Baddow, Chelmsford, Essex CM2 8HR. Tel: 01245 476444

Cheltenham – Hotel On The Park, Evesham Road, Cheltenham, Gloucestershire GL52 2AH. Tel: 01242 518898

Cheltenham (Charlton Kings) – The Cheltenham Park Hotel, Cirencester Road, Charlton Kings, Gloucestershire GL53 8EA. Tel: 01242 222021

Cheltenham (Shurdington) – The Greenway, Shurdington, Cheltenham, Gloucestershire GL51 5UG. Tel: 01242 862352

Chester – The Chester Grosvenor, Eastgate, Chester, Cheshire CH1 1LT. Tel: 01244 324024

Chester – Crabwall Manor, Parkgate Road, Mollington, Chester, Cheshire CH1 6NE. Tel: 01244 851666

Chester (Broxton) – Broxton Hall Country House Hotel, Whitchurch Road, Broxton, Chester, Cheshire CH3 9JS. Tel: 01829 782321

Chester (Carden) – Carden Park, Carden, Chester, Cheshire CH3 9DQ. Tel: 01829 731000

Chester (Northwich) – Nunsmere Hall, Tarporley Road, Oakmere, Northwich, Cheshire CW8 2ES. Tel: 01606 889100

Chester (Rowton) – Rowton Hall Hotel, Whitchurch Road, Rowton, Chester, Cheshire CH3 6AD. Tel: 01244 335262

Chichester (Bosham) – The Millstream Hotel, Bosham, Nr Chichester, West Sussex PO18 8HL. Tel: 01243 573234

Chipping Campden – Charingworth Manor, Nr Chipping Campden, Gloucestershire GL55 6NS. Tel: 01386 593555

Chipping Campden – The Noel Arms Hotel, High Street, Chipping Campden, Gloucestershire GL55 6AT. Tel: 01386 840317

Chipping Campden – The Cotswold House, High Street, Chipping Campden, Gloucestershire GL55 6AN. Tel: 01386 840330

Cirencester (Nr Stroud) – The Bear of Rodborough Hotel, Rodborough Common, Stroud, Nr Cirencester, Gloucestershire GL5 5DE. Tel: 01453 878522

Clanfield – The Plough at Clanfield, Bourton Road, Clanfield, Oxfordshire OX18 2RB. Tel: 01367 810222

Cobham (Stoke D'Abernon) – Woodlands Park Hotel, Woodlands Lane, Stoke d'Abernon, Cobham, Surrey KT11 3QB. Tel: 01372 843933

Colchester – Five Lakes Hotel Golf Country Club & Spa, Colchester Road,Whitehouse Hill, Tolleshunt Knights, Maldon, Essex CM9 8HX. Tel: 01621 868888

Coventry (Berkswell) – Nailcote Hall, Nailcote Lane, Berkswell, Nr Solihull, Warwickshire CV7 7DE. Tel: 024 76466174

Coventry (Binley) – Coombe Abbey, Brinklow Road, Binley, Warwickshire CV3 2AB. Tel: 024 76450450

Crathorne (Yarm) – Crathorne Hall Hotel, Crathorne, Nr Yarm, North Yorkshire TS15 0AR. Tel: 01642 700398

Cuckfield – Ockenden Manor, Ockenden Lane, Cuckfield, West Sussex RH17 5LD. Tel: 01444 416111

Darlington (Gainford) – Headlam Hall, Headlam, Darlington, Nr Gainford, County Durham DL2 3HA. Tel: 01325 730238

Dartford (Wilmington) – Rowhill Grange, Wilmington, Dartford, Kent DA2 7QH. Tel: 01322 615136

Dartmoor (Haytor Vale) – Bel Alp House, Haytor , Nr Bovey Tracey, Devon TQ13 9XX. Tel: 01364 661217

Daventry (Fawsley) – Fawsley Hall Hotel, Fawsley, Nr Daventry, Northamptonshire NN11 3BA. Tel: 01327 892000

Dedham – Maison Talbooth, Stratford Road, Dedham, Colchester, Essex CO7 6HN. Tel: 01206 322367

Derby – Mickleover Court, Etwall Road, Mickleover, Derbyshire DE3 5XX. Tel: 01332 521234

Derby (Castle Donington) – The Priest House On the River, Kings Mills, Castle Donington, Derbyshire DE74 2RR. Tel: 01332 810649

Derby (Milford) – Makeney Hall Country House Hotel, Makeney, Milford, Derbyshire DE56 0RS. Tel: 01332 842999

Derby (Risley) – Risley Hall Country House Hotel, Derby Road, Risley, Derbyshire DE72 3SS. Tel: 0115 939 9000

Durham (Chester-Le-Street) – Lumley Castle Hotel, Chester-Le-Street, County Durham DH3 4NX. Tel: 0191 389 1111

Easington – Grinkle Park Hotel, Easington, Saltburn-by-the-Sea, Cleveland TS13 4UB. Tel: 01287 640515

Eastbourne – The Grand Hotel, King Edward's Parade, Eastbourne, East Sussex BN21 4EQ. Tel: 01323 412345

Egham – Great Fosters, Stroude Road, Egham, Surrey TW20 9UR. Tel: 01784 433822

Evershot (Nr Dorchester) – Summer Lodge, Summer Lane, Evershot, Dorset DT2 0JR. Tel: 01935 83424

Evesham – The Evesham Hotel, Coopers Lane, Off Waterside, Evesham, Worcestershire WR11 6DA. Tel: 01386 765566

Evesham (Wood Norton) – Wood Norton Hall, Wood Norton, Evesham, Worcestershire WR11 4YB. Tel: 01386 420007

Exeter – St Olaves Court Hotel, Mary Arches Street, Exeter, Devon EX4 3AZ. Tel: 01392 217736

Exeter (Honiton) – Combe House at Gittisham, Honiton, Nr Exeter, Devon EX14 0AD. Tel: 01404 540400

Falmouth – Penmere Manor, Mongleath Road, Falmouth, Cornwall TR11 4PN. Tel: 01326 211411

Falmouth (Mawnan Smith) – Budock Vean Golf & Country House Hotel, Helford River, Mawnan Smith, Falmouth, Cornwall TR11 5LG. Tel: 01326 250288

Falmouth (Mawnan Smith) – Meudon Hotel, Mawnan Smith, Falmouth, Cornwall TR11 5HT. Tel: 01326 250541

Forest Row – Ashdown Park Hotel & Country Club, Wych Cross, Forest Row, East Sussex RH18 5JR. Tel: 01342 824988

Fowey – Fowey Hall Hotel & Restaurant, Hanson Drive, Fowey, Cornwall PL23 1ET. Tel: 01726 833866

Gatwick (Horley) – Langshott Manor, Langshott, Horley, Surrey RH6 9LN. Tel: 01293 786680

Gatwick (Turner's Hill) – Alexander House, East Street, Turner's Hill, West Sussex RH10 4QD. Tel: 01342 714914

Glossop – The Wind In The Willows, Derbyshire Level, Glossop, Derbyshire SK13 9PT. Tel: 01457 868001

Grange-Over-Sands – Graythwaite Manor, Fernhill Road, Grange-Over-Sands, Cumbria LA11 7JE. Tel: 015395 32001

Grasmere – Michaels Nook, Grasmere, Cumbria LA22 9RP. Tel: 015394 35496

Grasmere – The Wordsworth Hotel, Grasmere, Near Ambleside, Cumbria LA22 9SW. Tel: 015394 35592

Grayshott – Grayshott Hall Health Fitness Retreat, Headley Road, Grayshott, Nr Hindhead, Surrey GU26 6JJ. Tel: 01428 602000

Guildford – The Angel Posting House And Livery, 91 The High Street, Guildford, Surrey GU1 3DP. Tel: 01483 564555

Hadley Wood – West Lodge Park, Cockfosters Road, Hadley Wood, Barnet, Hertfordshire EN4 0PY. Tel: 020 8216 3900

Halifax (Holmfield) – Holdsworth House, Holdsworth Road, Holmfield, Halifax, West Yorkshire HX2 9TG. Tel: 01422 240024

Hampstead Village (London) – Sandringham Hotel, 3 Holford Road, Hampstead Village, London, NW3 1AD. Tel: 020 7435 1569

Hampton Court – The Carlton Mitre Hotel, Hampton Court Road, Hampton Court, Surrey KT8 9BN. Tel: 020 8979 9988

Harrogate – The Balmoral Hotel, Franklin Mount, Harrogate, North Yorkshire HG1 5EJ. Tel: 01423 508208

Harrogate – Grants Hotel, Swan Road, Harrogate, North Yorkshire HG1 2SS. Tel: 01423 560666

Harrogate – Rudding Park House & Hotel, Rudding Park, Follifoot, Harrogate, North Yorkshire HG3 1JH. Tel: 01423 871350

Harrogate (Markington) – Hob Green Hotel & Restaurant, Markington, Harrogate, North Yorkshire HG3 3PJ. Tel: 01423 770031

Harrogate (Ripley Castle) – The Boar's Head Hotel, Ripley, Harrogate, North Yorkshire HG3 3AY. Tel: 01423 771888

Haslemere – Lythe Hill Hotel, Petworth Road, Haslemere, Surrey GU27 3BQ. Tel: 01428 651251

Hathersage – George Hotel, Main Road, Hathersage, Derbyshire S32 1BB. Tel: 01433 650436

Hawes (Upper Wensleydale) – Simonstone Hall, Hawes, North Yorkshire DL8 3LY. Tel: 01969 667255

Hazlewood – Hazlewood Castle Hotel, Paradise Lane, Hazlewood, Nr Tadcaster, North Yorkshire LS24 9NJ. Tel: 01937 535353

Heathrow – Stoke Park, Park Road, Stoke Poges, Buckinghamshire SL2 4PG. Tel: 01753 717171

Helmsley (Harome) – The Pheasant, Harome, Helmsley, North Yorkshire YO62 5JG. Tel: 01439 771241 /770416

Henley-On-Thames – Phyllis Court Club, Marlow Road, Henley-On-Thames, Oxfordshire RG9 2HT. Tel: 01491 570500

Hockley Heath – Nuthurst Grange, Hockley Heath, Warwickshire B94 5NL. Tel: 01564 783972

Horsham (Nr Gatwick) – South Lodge Hotel, Brighton Road, Lower Beeding, Nr Horsham, West Sussex RH13 6PS. Tel: 01403 891711

Hovingham (Near York) – The Worsley Arms Hotel, Hovingham, York, North Yorkshire YO6 4LA. Tel: 01653 628234

Huddersfield (Denby Dale) – Bagden Hall Hotel & Golf Course, Wakefield Road, Scissett, Nr Huddersfield, West Yorkshire HD8 9LE. Tel: 01484 865330

Hull (Willerby) – Willerby Manor Hotel, Well Lane, Willerby, East Yorkshire HU10 6ER. Tel: 01482 652616

Ilkley – Rombalds Hotel, West View, Wells Road, Ilkley, West Yorkshire LS29 9JG. Tel: 01943 603201

Ilsington (Dartmoor) – Ilsington Country Hotel, Ilsington, Newton Abbot, Devon TQ13 9RR. Tel: 01364 661452

Ipswich – The Marlborough Hotel, Henley Road, Ipswich, Suffolk IP1 3SP. Tel: 01473 257677

Ipswich (Belstead) – Swallow Belstead Brook Hotel, Belstead Road, Ipswich, Suffolk IP2 9HB. Tel: 01473 682891

Ipswich (Hintlesham) – Hintlesham Hall, Hintlesham, Ipswich, Suffolk IP8 3NS. Tel: 01473 652268

Keswick (Grange-in-Borrowdale) – The Borrowdale Gates Country House Hotel, Grange-in-Borrowdale, Keswick, Cumbria CA12 5UQ. Tel: 017687 77204

Kettering (Northamptonshire) – Kettering Park Hotel, Kettering Parkway, Kettering, Northamptonshire NN15 6XT. Tel: 01536 416666

Kidderminster (Stone) – Stone Manor Hotel, Stone, Kidderminster, Worcestershire DY10 4PJ. Tel: 01562 777555

King's Lynn (Grimston) – Congham Hall, Grimston, King's Lynn, Norfolk PE32 1AH. Tel: 01485 600250

Kingham – Mill House Hotel, Kingham, Oxfordshire OX7 6UH. Tel: 01608 658188

Kingsbridge Estuary (Goveton) – Buckland-Tout-Saints, Goveton, Kingsbridge, Devon TQ7 2DS. Tel: 01548 853055

Knutsford – Mere Court Hotel, Warrington Road, Mere, Knutsford, Cheshire WA16 0RW. Tel: 01565 831000

Lacock – Beechfield House, Beanacre, Nr Lacock, Wiltshire SN12 7PU. Tel: 01225 703700

Lake Ullswater – Sharrow Bay Country House Hotel, Howtown, Lake Ullswater, Penrith, Cumbria CA10 2LZ. Tel: 017684 86301

Lake Ullswater (Watermillock) – Rampsbeck Country House Hotel, Watermillock, Lake Ullswater, Nr Penrith, Cumbria CA11 0LP. Tel: 017684 86442

Leamington Spa (Bishops Tachbrook) – Mallory Court, Harbury Lane, Bishops Tachbrook, Leamington Spa, Warwickshire CV33 9QB. Tel: 01926 330214

Leeds – Haley's Hotel and Restaurant, Shire Oak Road, Headingley, Leeds, West Yorkshire LS6 2DE. Tel: 0113 278 4446

Leeds – Oulton Hall, Rothwell Lane, Oulton, Leeds, West Yorkshire LS26 8HN. Tel: 0113 282 1000

Leeds (City Centre) – 42 The Calls, 42 The Calls, Leeds, West Yorkshire LS2 7EW. Tel: 0113 244 0099

Leicester (Hinkley) – Sketchley Grange Hotel, Sketchley Lane, Burbage, Hinkley, Leicestershire LE10 3HU. Tel: 01455 251133

Lewdown – Lewtrenchard Manor, Lewdown, Nr Okehampton, Devon EX20 4PN. Tel: 01566 783 256

Lewes (Newick) – Newick Park, Newick, Near Lewes, Sussex BN8 4SB. Tel: 01825 723633

Lichfield (Hoar Cross) – Hoar Cross Hall Health Spa Resort, Hoar Cross, Nr Yoxall, Staffordshire DE13 8QS. Tel: 01283 575671

Lifton (Nr Launceston) – The Arundell Arms, Lifton, Devon PL16 0AA. Tel: 01566 784666

London – Brown's Hotel, Albemarle Street, London, W1A 4SW. Tel: 020 7493 6020

London (Chelsea) – Chelsea Green Hotel, 35 Ixworth Place, London, SW3 3QX. Tel: 020 7225 7500

London (Chelsea) – Draycott House Apartments, 10 Draycott Avenue, Chelsea, London, SW3 3AA. Tel: 020 7584 4659

London (City) – London Bridge Hotel & Apartments, 81 London Bridge Street, London, SE1 9SG. Tel: 020 7855 2200

London (Covent Garden) – One Aldwych, London, WC2B 4BZ. Tel: 020 7300 1000

London (Cruise Ship) – Swan Hellenic Minerva, 77 New Oxford Street, London, WC1 1PP. Tel: 020 7800 2227

London (Hendon) – Hendon Hall, Ashley Lane, off Parsons Street, Hendon, London, NW4 1HF. Tel: 020 8203 3341

London (Kensington) – Chequers of Kensingtonir, 58-66 Cromwell Road, London, SW7 5BA. Tel: 020 7969 3555

London (Kensington) – Harrington Hall, 5-25 Harrington Gardens, London, SW7 4JW. Tel: 020 7396 9696

London (Kensington) – The Lexham Apartments, 32-38 Lexham Gardens, Kensington, London, W8 5JE. Tel: 020 7559 4444

London (Kensington) – The Milestone Hotel, 1 Kensington Court, London, W8 5DL. Tel: 020 7917 1000

London (Kensington) – Pembridge Court Hotel, 34 Pembridge Gardens, London, W2 4DX. Tel: 020 7229 9977

London (Kensington) – Twenty Nevern Square, London, SW5 9PD. Tel: 020 7565 9555

London (Knightsbridge) – Basil Street Hotel, Basil Street, London, SW3 1AH. Tel: 020 7581 3311

London (Knightsbridge) – The Beaufort, 33 Beaufort Gardens, Knightsbridge, London, SW3 1PP. Tel: 020 7584 5252

London (Knightsbridge) – Beaufort House Apartments, 45 Beaufort Gardens, London, SW3 1PN. Tel: 020 7584 2600

London (Knightsbridge) – The Cadogan, Sloane Street, London, SW1X 9SG. Tel: 020 7235 7141

London (Knightsbridge) – The Cliveden Town House, 26 Cadogan Gardens, London , SW3 2RP. Tel: 020 7730 6466

London (Knightsbridge) – Number Eleven Cadogan Gardens, 11 Cadogan Gardens, Sloane Square Knightsbridge, London, SW3 2RJ. Tel: 020 7730 7000

London (Lancaster Gate) – Fountains, 1 Lancaster Terrace, Hyde Park, London, W2 3PF. Tel: 020 7706 7070

London (Lancaster Gate) – The Hempel, Hempel Garden Square, 31-35 Craven Hill Gardens, London, W2 3EA. Tel: 020 7298 9000

London (Little Venice) – The Colonnade Town House, 2 Warrington Crescent, London W9 1ER. Tel: 020 7286 1052

London (Mayfair) – The Ascott Mayfair, 49 Hill Street, London, W1X 7FQ. Tel: 020 7499 6868

London (Mayfair) – Claridge's, Brook Street, Mayfair, London, W1A 2JQ. Tel: 020 7629 8860

London (Mayfair) – The Dorchester, Park Lane, Mayfair, London, WIA 2HJ. Tel: 020 7629 8888

London (Mayfair) – No 5 Maddox Street, 5 Maddox Street, London, W1R 9LE. Tel: 020 7647 0200

London (Mayfair) – Westbury Hotel, Bond Street, London, W1A 4UH. Tel: 020 7629 7755

London (Portman Square) – The Leonard, 15 Seymour Street, London, W1H 5AA. Tel: 020 7935 2010

London (South Kensington) – Blakes Hotel, 33 Roland Gardens, London, SW7 3PF. Tel: 020 7370 6701

London (South Kensington) – Number Sixteen, 16 Sumner Place, London, SW7 3EG. Tel: 020 7589 5232

London (Whitehall) – The Royal Horseguards, Whitehall Court, London, SW1A 2EJ. Tel: 020 7839 3400

London (Wimbledon Common) – Cannizaro House, West Side, Wimbledon Common, London, SW19 4UE. Tel: 020 8879 1464

Loughborough (Quorn) – Quorn Country Hotel, 66 Leicester Road, Quorn, Leicestershire LE12 8BB. Tel: 01509 415050

Louth – Kenwick Park Hotel & Leisure Club, Kenwick Park, Louth, Lincolnshire LN1 8NR. Tel: 01507 608806

Lower Slaughter – Washbourne Court Hotel , Lower Slaughter, Gloucestershire GL54 2HS. Tel: 01451 822143

Ludlow – Dinham Hall, Ludlow, Shropshire SY8 1EJ. Tel: 01584 876464

Lymington – Passford House Hotel, Mount Pleasant Lane, Lymington, Hampshire SO41 8LS. Tel: 01590 682398

Lymington – Stanwell House, High Street, Lymington, Hampshire SO41 9AA. Tel: 01590 677123

Lyndhurst – Parkhill Country House Hotel, Beaulieu Road, Lyndhurst, New Forest, Hampshire SO43 7FZ. Tel: 023 80282944

Macclesfield (Pott Shrigley) – Shrigley Hall Hotel Golf & Country Club, Shrigley Park, Pott Shrigley, Nr Macclesfield, Cheshire SK10 5SB. Tel: 01625 575757

Maidenhead – Fredrick's Hotel & Restaurant, Shoppenhangers Road, Maidenhead, Berkshire SL6 2PZ. Tel: 01628 581000

Maidenhead (Taplow) – Cliveden, Taplow, Berkshire SL6 0JF. Tel: 01628 668561

Maidenhead (Taplow) – Taplow House Hotel, Berry Hill, Taplow, Nr Maidenhead, Berkshire SL6 0DA. Tel: 01628 670056

Maidstone (Lenham) – Chilston Park, Sandway, Lenham, Maidstone, Kent ME17 2BE. Tel: 01622 859803

Malmesbury – The Old Bell, Abbey Row, Malmesbury, Wiltshire SN16 0AG. Tel: 01666 822344

Malmesbury – Whatley Manor, Easton Grey, Malmesbury, Wiltshire SN16 0RB. Tel: 01666 822888

Malmesbury (Crudwell) – Crudwell Court Hotel, Crudwell, Malmesbury, Wiltshire SN16 9EP. Tel: 01666 577194

Malvern (Colwall) – The Colwall Park Hotel, Colwall, Nr Malvern, Worcestershire WR12 6QG. Tel: 01684 540206

Malvern Wells – The Cottage In The Wood, Holywell Road, Malvern Wells, Worcestershire WR14 4LG. Tel: 01684 575859

Manchester Airport – Etrop Grange, Thorley Lane, Manchester Airport, Greater Manchester M90 4EG. Tel: 0161 499 0500

Manchester (Wilmslow) – The Stanneylands Hotel, Stanneylands Road, Wilmslow, Cheshire SK9 4EY. Tel: 01625 525225

Marlborough – Ivy House Hotel, High Street, Marlborough, Wiltshire SN8 1HJ. Tel: 01672 515333

Marlow-On-Thames – Danesfield House, Henley Road, Marlow-On-Thames, Buckinghamshire SL7 2EY. Tel: 01628 891010

Marston (Grantham) – The Olde Barn Hotel, Toll Bar Road, Marston, Lincolnshire NG32 2HT. Tel: 01400 250909

Matlock (Riber) – Riber Hall, Matlock, Derbyshire DE4 5JU. Tel: 01629 582795

Melton Mowbray – Stapleford Park, An Outpost of The Carnegie Club, Nr Melton Mowbray, Leicestershire LE14 2EF. Tel: 01572 787522

Middlecombe (Minehead) – Periton Park Hotel, Middlecombe, Nr Minehead, Somerset TA24 8SN. Tel: 01643 706885

Midhurst – The Angel Hotel, North Street, Midhurst, West Sussex GU29 9DN. Tel: 01730 812421

Midhurst – The Spread Eagle Hotel & Health Spa, South Street, Midhurst, West Sussex GU29 9NH . Tel: 01730 816911

Milton Keynes (Aspley Guise) – Moore Place Hotel, The Square, Aspley Guise, Milton Keynes, Bedfordshire MK17 8DW. Tel: 01908 282000

Moreton-In-Marsh – The Manor House Hotel, Moreton-In-Marsh, Gloucestershire GL56 0LJ. Tel: 01608 650501

Nantwich – Rookery Hall, Worleston, Nantwich, Nr Chester, Cheshire CW5 6DQ. Tel: 01270 610016

Newbury – Donnington Valley Hotel & Golf Course, Old Oxford Road, Donnington, Newbury, Berkshire RG14 3AG. Tel: 01635 551199

Newbury – Hollington House Hotel, Woolton Hill, Nr Newbury, Berkshire RG20 9XA. Tel: 01635 255100

Newbury – The Vineyard At Stockcross, Newbury, Berkshire RG20 8JU. Tel: 01635 528770

Newcastle-Upon-Tyne (Morpeth) – Linden Hall Hotel, Health Spa & Golf Course, Longhorsley, Morpeth, Newcastle-Upon - Tyne, Northumberland NE65 8XF. Tel: 01670 516611

Newmarket – Swynford Paddocks Hotel & Restaurant, Six Mile Bottle, Newmarket, Suffolk CB8 0UE. Tel: 01638 570234

Newton Aycliffe – Redworth Hall Hotel & Country Club, Redworth, Nr Newton Aycliffe, County Durham DL5 6NL. Tel: 01388 772442

Norwich – Swallow Sprowston Manor Hotel, Sprowston Park, Wroxham Road, Norwich, Norfolk NR7 8RP. Tel: 01603 789409

Norwich (Hethersett) – Park Farm Hotel & Leisure, Hethersett, Norwich, Norfolk NR9 3DL. Tel: 01603 810264

Norwich (Horning) – Petersfield House Hotel, Lower Street, Horning, Norwich, Norfolk NR12 8PF. Tel: 01692 630741

Nottingham (Langar) – Langar Hall, Langar, Nottinghamshire NG13 9HG. Tel: 01949 860559

Oakham – Hambleton Hall, Hambleton, Oakham, Rutland LE15 8TH. Tel: 01572 756991

Otley – Chevin Lodge Country Park Hotel, Yorkgate, Otley, West Yorkshire LS21 3NU. Tel: 01943 467818

Ottershaw – Foxhills, Stonehill Road, Ottershaw, Surrey KT16 0EL. Tel: 01932 704500

Oxford (Great Milton) – Le Manoir aux Quat' Saisons, Great Milton, Oxfordshire OX44 7PD. Tel: 01844 278881

Oxford (Horton-cum-Studley) – Studley Priory, Horton Hill, Horton-cum-Studley, Oxford, Oxfordshire OX33 1AZ. Tel: 01865 351203

Oxford (Kingston Bagpuize) – Fallowfields, Kingston Bagpuize With Southmoor, Oxfordshire OX13 5BH. Tel: 01865 820416

Oxford (Weston-on-the-Green) – Weston Manor, Weston-on-the-Green, Oxfordshire OX6 8QL. Tel: 01869 350621

Painswick – The Painswick Hotel, Kemps Lane, Painswick, Gloucestershire GL6 6YB. Tel: 01452 812160

Peterborough (Wansford) – The Haycock, Wansford-In-England, Peterborough , Cambridgeshire PE8 6JA. Tel: 01780 782223

Polperro (Talland Bay) – Talland Bay Hotel, Talland-By-Looe, Cornwall PL13 2JB. Tel: 01503 272667

Prestbury – The Bridge Hotel, Prestbury, Macclesfield, Cheshire SK10 4DQ. Tel: 01625 829326

Preston (Chipping) – The Gibbon Bridge Country House Hotel, Chipping, Forest of Bowland, Lancashire PR3 2TQ. Tel: 01995 61456

Redhill (Nr Gatwick) – Nutfield Priory, Nutfield, Redhill, Surrey RH1 4EN. Tel: 01737 824400

Richmond-Upon-Thames – The Richmond Gate Hotel And Restaurant , Richmond Hill, Richmond-Upon-Thames, Surrey TW10 6RP. Tel: 020 8940 0061

Ross-On-Wye – The Chase Hotel, Gloucester Road, Ross-On-Wye, Herefordshire HR9 5LH. Tel: 01989 763161

Ross-On-Wye (Pengethley) – Pengethley Manor, Pengethley Park, Nr Ross-On-Wye, Herefordshire HR9 6LL. Tel: 01989 730211

Rusper (Near Gatwick) – Ghyll Manor Country Hotel, High Street, Rusper, Near Horsham, Sussex RH12 4PX. Tel: 01293 871571

Rutland Water – Barnsdale Lodge, The Avenue, Rutland Water, Nr Oakham, Rutland, Leicestershire LE15 8AH. Tel: 01572 724678

Rye (Rye Foreign) – Broomhill Lodge, Rye Foreign, Rye, East Sussex TN31 7UN. Tel: 01797 280421

Salcombe – Bolt Head Hotel, South Sands, Salcombe, Devon TQ8 8LL. Tel: 01548 843751

Salcombe (Soar Mill Cove) – Soar Mill Cove Hotel, Soar Mill Cove, Salcombe, Devon TQ7 3DS. Tel: 01548 561566

Salcombe (South Sands) – The Tides Reach Hotel, South Sands, Salcombe, Devon TQ8 8LJ. Tel: 01548 843466

Salisbury (Teffont Evias) – Howard's House, Teffont Evias, Salisbury, Wiltshire SP3 5RJ. Tel: 01722 716392

Scarborough (Hackness) – Hackness Grange, North York Moors National Park, Scarborough, North Yorkshire YO13 0JW. Tel: 01723 882345

Scarborough (Scalby) – Wrea Head Country Hotel, Scalby, Nr Scarborough, North Yorkshire YO13 0PB. Tel: 01723 378211

Seaview (Isle of Wight) – The Priory Bay Hotel, Priory Drive, Sea View, Isle of Wight PO34 5BU. Tel: 01983 613146

Sheffield – Charnwood Hotel, 10 Sharrow Lane, Sheffield, South Yorkshire S11 8AA. Tel: 0114 258 9411

Sheffield (Grenoside) – Whitley Hall Hotel, Elliot Lane, Grenoside, Sheffield, South Yorkshire S35 8NR. Tel: 0114 245 4444

Sheffield (Hellaby) – Hellaby Hall Hotel, Old Hellaby Lane, Hellaby, Nr Sheffield, South Yorkshire S66 8SN. Tel: 01709 702701

Shepton Mallet – Charlton House and The Mulberry Restaurant, Charlton Road, Shepton Mallet, Nr Bath, Somerset BA4 4PR. Tel: 01749 342008

Shrewsbury – Rowton Castle, Shrewsbury, Shropshire SY5 9EP. Tel: 01743 884044

Shrewsbury (Albrighton) – Albrighton Hall Hotel & Restaurant, Albrighton, Shrewsbury, Shropshire SY4 3AG. Tel: 01939 291000

Shrewsbury (Weston-under-Redcastle) – Hawkstone Park Hotel, Weston-under-Redcastle, Shrewsbury, Shropshire SY4 5UY. Tel: 01939 200611

Sidmouth – Hotel Riviera, The Esplanade, Sidmouth, Devon EX10 8AY. Tel: 01395 515201

Sonning-On-Thames – The French Horn, Sonning-on-Thames, Berkshire RG4 0TN. Tel: 01189 692204

South Molton – Whitechapel Manor, Nr South Molton, North Devon EX36 3EG. Tel: 01769 573377

Southwold – The Swan Hotel, Market Place, Southwold, Suffolk IP18 6EG. Tel: 01502 722186

St Agnes (Mithian) – Rose-in-Vale Country House Hotel, Mithian, St Agnes, Cornwall TR5 0QD. Tel: 01872 552202

St Albans – Sopwell House Hotel Country Club & Spa, Cottonmill Lane, Sopwell, St Albans, Hertfordshire AL1 2HQ. Tel: 01727 864477

St. Ives – The Garrack Hotel & Restaurant, Burthallan Lane, St Ives, Cornwall TR26 3AA. Tel: 01736 796199

St Keyne – The Well House, St Keyne, Liskeard, Cornwall PL14 4RN. Tel: 01579 342001

St.Mawes (Porthcurnick Beach) – The Rosevine Hotel, Porthcurnick Beach, Portscatho, St.Mawes, Truro, TR2 5EW. Tel: 01872 580206

Stamford – The George Of Stamford, St Martins, Stamford, Lincolnshire PE9 2LB. Tel: 01780 750750

Stansted – Whitehall, Church End, Broxted, Essex CM6 2BZ. Tel: 01279 850603

Stonehouse – Stonehouse Court, Stonehouse, Gloucestershire GL10 3RA. Tel: 01453 825155

Stow-On-The-Wold – The Grapevine Hotel, Sheep Street, Stow-On-The-Wold, Gloucestershire GL54 1AU. Tel: 01451 830344

Stow-On-The-Wold – Wyck Hill House, Wyck Hill, Stow-On-The-Wold, Gloucestershire GL54 1HY. Tel: 01451 831936

Stow-on-the-Wold (Upper Slaughter) – Lords Of The Manor Hotel, Upper Slaughter, Nr Bourton-On-The-Water, Gloucestershire GL54 2JD. Tel: 01451 820243

Stratford-Upon-Avon – Billesley Manor, Billesley, Alcester, Nr Stratford-Upon-Avon, Warwickshire B49 6NF. Tel: 01789 279955

Stratford-Upon-Avon – Ettington Park, Alderminster, Stratford-Upon-Avon, Warwickshire CV37 8BU. Tel: 01789 450123

Stratford-Upon-Avon – Welcombe Hotel & Golf Course , Warwick Road, Stratford-Upon-Avon, Warwickshire CV37 0NR. Tel: 01789 295252

Stratford-Upon-Avon (Abbot's Salford) – Salford Hall Hotel, Abbot's Salford, Evesham, Worcestershire WR11 5UT. Tel: 01386 871300

Streatley-On-Thames (Reading) – The Swan Diplomat, Streatley-On-Thames, Reading, Berkshire RG8 9HR. Tel: 01491 873737

Sturminster Newton – Plumber Manor, Sturminster Newton, Dorset DT10 2AF. Tel: 01258 472507

Swindon (Purton) – The Pear Tree at Purton, Church End, Purton, Nr Swindon, Wiltshire SN5 9ED. Tel: 01793 772100

Taunton – The Castle At Taunton, Castle Green, Taunton, Somerset TA1 1AF. Tel: 01823 272671

Taunton (Henlade) – The Mount Somerset Country House Hotel, Henlade, Taunton, Somerset TA3 5NB. Tel: 01823 442500

Taunton (Langford Budville) – Bindon Country House Hotel & Restaurant, Langford Budville, Wellington, Somerset TA21 0RU. Tel: 01823 400070

Tavistock (Gulworthy) – The Horn Of Plenty, Gulworthy, Tavistock, Devon PL19 8JD. Tel: 01822 832528

Telford (Ironbridge) – Madeley Court, Telford, Shropshire TF7 5DW. Tel: 01952 680068

Tetbury – Calcot Manor, Nr Tetbury, Gloucestershire GL8 8YJ. Tel: 01666 890391

Tetbury – The Close Hotel, Long Street, Tetbury, Gloucestershire GL8 8AQ. Tel: 01666 502272

Tewkesbury (Corse Lawn) – Corse Lawn House Hotel, Corse Lawn, Nr Tewkesbury , Gloucestershire GL19 4LZ. Tel: 01452 780479 / 771

Thame – The Spread Eagle Hotel, Cornmarket, Thame, Oxfordshire OX9 2BW. Tel: 01844 213661

Thirsk – Crab Manor, Asenby, North Yorkshire YO7 3QL. Tel: 01845 577286

Ticehurst (Nr Tunbridge Wells) – Dale Hill, Ticehurst, Wadhurst, East Sussex TN5 7DQ. Tel: 01580 200112

Torquay – The Palace Hotel, Babbacombe Road, Torquay, Devon TQ1 3TG. Tel: 01803 200200

Torquay (Meadfoot) – The Osborne Hotel & Langtry's Restaurant, Meadfoot Beach, Torquay, Devon TQ1 2LL. Tel: 01803 213311

Tring – Pendley Manor Hotel & Conference Centre, Cow Lane, Tring, Hertfordshire HP23 5QY. Tel: 01442 891891

Tunbridge Wells – Hotel Du Vin & Bistro, Crescent Road, Royal Tunbridge Wells, Kent TN1 2LY. Tel: 01892 526455

Tunbridge Wells – The Spa Hotel, Mount Ephraim, Royal Tunbridge Wells, Kent TN4 8XJ. Tel: 01892 520331

Uckfield (Little Horsted) – Horsted Place Hotel, Little Horsted, Nr Uckfield, East Sussex TN22 5TS. Tel: 01825 750581

Uppingham – The Lake Isle, 16 High Street East, Uppingham, Rutland LE15 9PZ. Tel: 01572 822951

Veryan (Nr St Mawes) – The Nare Hotel, Carne Beach, Veryan-In-Roseland, Truro, Cornwall TR2 5PF. Tel: 01872 501279

Wallingford (North Stoke) – The Springs Hotel & Golf Club, North Stoke, Wallingford, Oxfordshire OX10 6BE. Tel: 01491 836687

Ware – Hanbury Manor, Ware, Hertfordshire SG12 0SD. Tel: 01920 487722

Wareham – The Priory, Church Green, Wareham, Dorset BH20 4ND. Tel: 01929 551666

Warminster – Bishopstrow House, Warminster, Wiltshire BA12 9HH. Tel: 01985 212312

Warwick (Barford) – The Glebe At Barford, Church Street, Barford, Warwickshire CV35 8BS. Tel: 01926 624218

Wetherby – Wood Hall, Linton, Near Wetherby, West Yorkshire LS22 4JA. Tel: 01937 587271

Weybridge – Oatlands Park Hotel, 146 Oatlands Drive, Weybridge, Surrey KT13 9HB. Tel: 01932 847242

Weymouth (Fleet) – Moonfleet Manor, Fleet, Weymouth, Dorset DT3 4ED. Tel: 01305 786948

Winchester – Hotel Du Vin & Bistro, Southgate Street, Winchester, Hampshire SO23 9EF. Tel: 01962 841414

Winchester (Sparsholt) – Lainston House Hotel, Sparsholt, Winchester, Hampshire SO21 2LT. Tel: 01962 863588

Windermere – Gilpin Lodge, Crook Road, Near Windermere, Cumbria LA23 3NE. Tel: 015394 88818

Windermere – Langdale Chase, Windermere, Cumbria LA23 1LW. Tel: 015394 32201

Windermere – Miller Howe, Rayrigg Road, Windermere, Cumbria LA23 1EY. Tel: 015394 42536

Windermere – Storrs Hall, Windermere, Cumbria LA23 3LG. Tel: 015394 47111

Windermere (Bowness) – Linthwaite House Hotel, Crook Road, Bowness-On-Windermere, Cumbria LA23 3JA. Tel: 015394 88600

Windermere (Newby Bridge) – Lakeside Hotel On Lake Windermere, Lakeside, Newby Bridge, Cumbria LA12 8AT. Tel: 0541 541586

Windsor – Sir Christopher Wren's Hotel & Business Centre, Thames Street, Windsor, Berkshire SL4 1PX. Tel: 01753 861354

Woburn – The Bedford Arms, George Street, Milton Keynes, Bedfordshire MK17 9PX. Tel: 01525 290441

Woburn (Flitwick) – Flitwick Manor, Church Road, Flitwick, Bedfordshire MK45 1AE. Tel: 01525 712242

Wolverhampton (Worfield) – The Old Vicarage Hotel, Worfield, Bridgnorth, Shropshire WV15 5JZ. Tel: 01746 716497

Woodbridge – Seckford Hall, Woodbridge, Suffolk IP13 6NU. Tel: 01394 385678

Woodstock – The Feathers Hotel, Market Street, Woodstock, Oxfordshire OX20 1SX. Tel: 01993 812291

Woolacombe – Woolacombe Bay Hotel, South Street, Woolacombe, Devon EX34 7BN. Tel: 01271 870388

Woolacombe (Mortehoe) – Watersmeet Hotel, Mortehoe, Woolacombe, Devon EX34 7EB. Tel: 01271 870333

Yarmouth (Isle of Wight) – The George Hotel, Quay Street, Yarmouth, Isle of Wight PO41 0PE. Tel: 01983 760331

York – The Grange Hotel, 1 Clifton, York, North Yorkshire YO30 6AA. Tel: 01904 644744

York – Middlethorpe Hall, Bishopthorpe Road, York, North Yorkshire YO23 2GB. Tel: 01904 641241

York – Mount Royale Hotel, The Mount, York, North Yorkshire YO2 2DA. Tel: 01904 628856

York (Monk Fryston) – Monk Fryston Hall, Monk Fryston, North Yorkshire LS25 5DU. Tel: 01977 682369

WALES

Aberdare (Hirwaun) – Ty Newydd Country Hotel, Penderyn Road, Hirwaun, Mid-Glamorgan CF44 9SX. Tel: 01685 813433

Abergavenny – Llansantffraed Court Hotel, Llanvihangel Gobion, Abergavenny, Monmouthshire NP7 9BA. Tel: 01873 840678

Abergavenny (Walterstone) – Allt-Yr-Ynys Hotel, Walterstone, Herefordshire HR2 0DU. Tel: 01873 890307

Abersoch – Porth Tocyn Country House Hotel, Abersoch, Pwllheli, Gwynedd LL53 7BU. Tel: 01758 713303

Aberystwyth – Conrah Country House Hotel, Rhydgaled, Chancery, Aberystwyth, Ceredigion SY23 4DF. Tel: 01970 617941

Anglesey (Trearddur Bay) – Trearddur Bay Hotel, Lon Issalt, Trearddur Bay, Anglesey, Holyhead, Gwynedd LL65 2UN. Tel: 01407 860301

Bala (Llandderfel) – Palé Hall, Llandderfel, Bala, Gwynedd LL23 7PS. Tel: 01678 530285

Barmouth (Bontddu) – Bontddu Hall, Bontddu, Barmouth, Gwynedd LL40 2UF. Tel: 01341 430661

Beaumaris – Ye Olde Bull's Head, Castle Street, Beaumaris, Anglesey, Gwynedd LL58 8AP. Tel: 01248 810329

Brecon (Llyswen) – Llangoed Hall, Llyswen, Brecon, Powys LD3 0YP. Tel: 01874 754525

Bridgend (Coychurch) – Coed-Y-Mwstwr Hotel, Coychurch, Nr Bridgend, Vale of Glamorgan CF35 6AF. Tel: 01656 860621

Cardiff – Miskin Manor, Miskin, Nr Cardiff, Mid Glamorgan CF72 8ND. Tel: 01443 224204

Chester (Ewloe) – St. David's Park Hotel, St. David's Park, Ewloe, Flintshire CH5 3YB. Tel: 01244 520800

Corwen (Llandrillo) – Tyddyn Llan Country House Hotel, Llandrillo, Nr Corwen, Denbighshire LL21 0ST. Tel: 01490 440264

Criccieth – Bron Eifion Country House Hotel, Criccieth, Gwynedd LL52 0SA. Tel: 01766 522385

Crickhowell – Gliffaes Country House Hotel, Crickhowell, Powys NP8 1RH. Tel: 01874 730371

Dolgellau (Penmaenpool) – Penmaenuchaf Hall, Penmaenpool, Dolgellau, Gwynedd LL40 1YB. Tel: 01341 422129

Harlech – Hotel Maes-Y-Neuadd, Talsarnau, Nr Harlech, Gwynedd LL47 6YA. Tel: 01766 780200

Lake Vyrnwy – Lake Vyrnwy Hotel, Lake Vyrnwy , Llanwddyn, Montgomeryshire SY10 0LY. Tel: 01691 870 692

Llandegla – Bodidris Hall, Llandegla, Wrexham, Denbighshire LL11 3AL. Tel: 01978 790434

Llandudno – Bodysgallen Hall, Llandudno, Gwynedd LL30 1RS. Tel: 01492 584466

Llandudno – St Tudno Hotel, Promenade, Llandudno, Gwynedd LL30 2LP. Tel: 01492 874411

Llangammarch Wells – The Lake Country House, Llangammarch Wells, Powys LD4 4BS. Tel: 01591 620202

Machynlleth – Ynyshir Hall, Eglwysfach, Machynlleth, Ceredigion SY20 8TA. Tel: 01654 781209

Pembroke – The Court Hotel & Restaurant, Lamphey, Pembroke, Nr Tenby, Pembrokeshire SA71 5NT. Tel: 01646 672273

Portmeirion Village – The Hotel Portmeirion, Portmeirion, Gwynedd LL48 6ET. Tel: 01766 770000

St David's – Warpool Court Hotel, St David's, Pembrokeshire SA62 6BN. Tel: 01437 720300

Tenby – Penally Abbey, Penally , Tenby, Pembrokeshire SA70 7PY. Tel: 01834 843033

Usk (Llangybi) – The Cwrt Bleddyn Hotel, Llangybi, Usk, Monmouthshire NP5 1PG. Tel: 01633 450521

Wrexham (Nr Chester) – Llyndir Hall Hotel, Llyndir Lane, Rossett, Nr Chester, Clwyd LL12 0AY. Tel: 01244 571648

SCOTLAND

Aberdeen – Ardoe House Hotel & Restaurant, South Deeside Road, Blairs, Aberdeen, Aberdeenshire AB10 5YP. Tel: 01224 867355

Aberdeen (Inverurie) – Thainstone House Hotel & Country Club, Inverurie, By Aberdeen, Aberdeenshire AB51 5NT. Tel: 01467 621643

Aberfoyle (Trossacks) – Forest Hills, Kinlochard, By Aberfoyle, The Trossacks, Stirlingshire FK8 3TL. Tel: 01877 387277

Angus (By Arbroath) – Letham Grange Resort, Colliston, By Arbroath, Angus DD11 4RL. Tel: 01241 890373

Auchencairn (Nr Castle Douglas) – Balcary Bay Hotel, Auchencairn, Nr Castle Douglas, Dumfries & Galloway DG7 1QZ. Tel: 01556 640217

Auchterarder – Auchterarder House, Auchterarder, Perthshire PH3 1DZ. Tel: 01764 663646

Ballantrae (Ayrshire) – Glenapp Castle, Ballantrae, Ayrshire KA26 0NZ. Tel: 01465 831212

Ballater (Royal Deeside) – Darroch Learg Hotel, Braemar Road, Ballater, Aberdeenshire AB35 5UX. Tel: 013397 55443

Banchory (Royal Deeside) – Raemoir House Hotel, Banchory, Royal Deeside, Aberdeenshire AB31 4ED. Tel: 01330 824884

Beasdale By Arisaig – Arisaig House, Beasdale, By Arisaig, Inverness-shire PH39 4NR. Tel: 01687 450622

Biggar – Shieldhill-Incorporating The Mennock Valley Shoot, Quothquan, Biggar, Lanarkshire ML12 6NA. Tel: 01899 220035

Blairgowrie – Kinloch House Hotel, By Blairgowrie, Perthshire PH10 6SG. Tel: 01250 884237

Callander – Roman Camp Hotel, Callander, Perthshire FK17 8BG. Tel: 01877 330003

Craigellachie (Speyside) – Craigellachie Hotel, Craigellachie, Speyside, Banffshire AB38 9SR. Tel: 01340 881204

Dunkeld – Kinnaird, Kinnaird Estate, By Dunkeld, Perthshire PH8 0LB. Tel: 01796 482 440

Dunoon – Enmore Hotel, Marine Parade, Kirn, Dunoon, Argyll PA23 8HH. Tel: 01369 702230

East Kilbride (Glasgow) – Macdonald Crutherland House Hotel, Strathaven Road, East Kilbride, Glasgow, Stathclyde G75 0QZ. Tel: 01355 577000

Edinburgh – The Bonham, 35 Drumsheugh Gardens, Edinburgh, Mid Lothian EH3 7RN. Tel: 0131 226 6050

Edinburgh – Channings, South Learmonth Gardens, Edinburgh, Mid Lothian EH4 1EZ. Tel: 0131 315 2226

Edinburgh – The Howard, 34 Great King Street, Edinburgh EH3 6QH. Tel: 0131 557 3500

Edinburgh – Prestonfield House, Priestfield Road, Edinburgh EH16 5UT. Tel: 0131 668 3346

Edinburgh – The Scotsman, Edinburgh. Tel: 0113 244 0099

Edinburgh (Bonnyrigg) – Dalhousie Castle , Bonnyrigg, Edinburgh EH19 3JB. Tel: 01875 820153

Edinburgh (Borthwick) – Borthwick Castle, Borthwick, North Middleton, Mid Lothian EH23 4QY. Tel: 01875 820514

Edinburgh (Ingliston) – The Norton House Hotel, Ingliston, Edinburgh, Mid Lothian EH28 8LX. Tel: 0131 333 1275

Elgin – Mansion House Hotel, The Haugh, Elgin, Moray, Inverness-shire IV30 1AW. Tel: 01343 548811

Fort William (Roy Bridge) – Glenspean Lodge Hotel, Roy Bridge, By Fort William, Inverness-shire PH31 4AW. Tel: 01397 712223

Gatehouse Of Fleet – Cally Palace Hotel, Gatehouse Of Fleet, Dumfries & Galloway DG7 2DL. Tel: 01557 814341

Glasgow – Carlton George Hotel, 44 West George Street, Glasgow G2 1DH. Tel: 0141 353 6373

Glasgow (Langbank) – Gleddoch House, Langbank, Renfrewshire PA14 6YE. Tel: 01475 540711

Glenshee (By Blairgowrie) – Dalmunzie House, Spittal O'Glenshee, Blairgowrie, Perthshire PH10 7QG. Tel: 01250 885224

Grantown-on-Spey (Dulnain Bridge) – Muckrach Lodge Hotel & Restaurant, Dulnain Bridge, By Grantown-on-Spey, Morayshire PH26 3LY. Tel: 01479 851257

Gullane – Greywalls, Muirfield, Gullane, East Lothian EH31 2EG. Tel: 01620 842144

Inverness – Bunchrew House Hotel, Inverness, Inverness-shire IV3 8TA. Tel: 01463 234917

Inverness – Swallow Kingsmills Hotel, Culcabock Road, Inverness, Inverness-shire IV2 3LP. Tel: 01463 237166

Inverness (Culloden) – Culloden House Hotel, Inverness, Inverness-shire IV2 7BZ. Tel: 01463 790461

Inverurie (Chapel of Gairoch) – Pittodrie House, Chapel of Gairoch, By Inverurie, Aberdeenshire AB51 5HS. Tel: 01467 681444

Isle Of Skye (Staffin) – Flodigarry Country House Hotel, Staffin, Isle Of Skye IV51 9HZ. Tel: 01470 552203

Kelso – Ednam House Hotel, Bridge Street, Kelso, Roxburghshire TD5 7HT. Tel: 01573 224168

Kelso – The Roxburghe Hotel & Golf Course, Kelso, Roxburghshire TD5 8JZ. Tel: 01573 450331

Kilchrenan by Taynuilt – Ardanaiseig, Kilchrenan by Taynuilt, Argyll PA35 1HE. Tel: 01866 833333

Kildrummy – Kildrummy Castle Hotel, Kildrummy, By Alford, Aberdeenshire AB33 8RA. Tel: 019755 71288

Kinbuck (Nr Stirling) – Cromlix House, Kinbuck, By Dunblane, Perthshire FK15 9JT. Tel: 01786 822125

Lochinver (Sutherland) – Inver Lodge Hotel, Lochinver, Sutherland IV27 4LK. Tel: 01571 844496

Newton Stewart – Kirroughtree House, Newton Stewart, Wigtownshire DG8 6AN. Tel: 01671 402141

Oban – Knipoch Hotel, By Oban, Argyll PA34 4QT. Tel: 01852 316251

Peebles – Cringletie House Hotel, Peebles, Peebleshire EH45 8PL. Tel: 01721 730233

Perth – Kinfauns Castle, Nr Perth, Perthshire PH2 7JZ. Tel: 01738 620777

Perth (Huntingtower) – Huntingtower Hotel, Crief Road, Perth, Perthshire PH1 3JT. Tel: 01738 583771

Perth (Kinclaven) – Ballathie House Hotel, Kinclaven, Perth, Perthshire PH1 4QN. Tel: 01250 883268

Pitlochry – Pine Trees Hotel, Strathview Terrace, Pitlochry, Tayside PH15 5QR. Tel: 01796 472121

Portpatrick – Fernhill Hotel, Heugh Road, Portpatrick, Wigtownshire DG8 8TD. Tel: 01776 810220

St. Andrews – St. Andrews Golf Hotel, 40 The Scores, St. Andrews, Fife KY16 9AS. Tel: 01334 472611

St Boswells (Melrose) – Dryburgh Abbey Hotel, St Boswells, Scottish Borders TD6 0RQ. Tel: 01835 822261

Stirling – Stirling Highland Hotel, Spittal Street, Stirling FK8 1DU. Tel: 01786 272727

Stranraer – Corsewall Lighthouse Hotel, Stranraer, Dunfries & Galloway DG9 0QG. Tel: 01776 853220

Strathpeffer (Contin) – Coul House Hotel, Contin, By Strathpeffer, Ross-shire IV14 9EY. Tel: 01997 421487

Tain (Highlands) – Mansfield House Hotel, Scotsburn Road, Tain, Ross-shire IV19 1PR. Tel: 01862 892052

Torridon (By Achnasheen) – Loch Torridon Hotel, Torridon , By Achnasheen, Wester-Ross, Inverness-shire IV22 2EY. Tel: 01445 791242

Troon – Marine Highland Hotel, Troon, Ayshire KA10 6HE. Tel: 01292 314444

Troon – Piersland House Hotel, Craigend Road, Troon, Ayrshire KA10 6HD. Tel: 01292 314747

Uphall (West Lothian) – Houstoun House, Uphall, West Lothian EH52 6JS. Tel: 01506 853831

IRELAND

Adare (Co Limerick) – Adare Manor, Adare, Co Limerick. Tel: 00 353 61 396566

Belfast (Northern Ireland) – The McCausland Hotel, 34-38 Victoria Street, Belfast BT1 3GH. Tel: 028 9022 0200

Carrickmacross (Co Monaghan) – Nuremore Hotel & Country Club, Carrickmacross, Co Monaghan IRELAND. Tel: 00 353 429 661438

Clonakilty (West Cork) – The Lodge & Spa at Inchydoney Island, Clonakilty, West Cork. Tel: 00 353 23 33143

Cong (Co. Mayo) – Ashford Castle, Cong, Co. Mayo. Tel: 00353 92 46003

Connemara (Co Galway) – Renvyle House Hotel, Renvyle, Connemara, Co Galway. Tel: 00 353 95 43511

Cork – Hayfield Manor Hotel, Perrott Avenue, College Road, Cork. Tel: 00 353 21 315600

Dublin – Brooks Hotel, 59-62 Drury Street, Dublin 2. Tel: 00 353 1 670 4000

Dublin – The Fitzwilliam Hotel, St. Stephens' Green, Dublin 2. Tel: 00 353 1 478 7000

Dublin – The Hibernian, Eastmoreland Place, Ballsbridge, Dublin 4. Tel: 00 353 1 668 7666

Dublin – The Merrion Hotel, Upper Merrion Street, Dublin 2, . Tel: 00 353 1 603 0600

Dublin (Portmarnock) – Portmarnock Hotel & Golf Links, Strand Road, Portmanock, Co Dublin. Tel: 00 353 1 846 0611

Dublin (Straffan) – Kildare Hotel & Country Club, At Straffan, Co Kildare. Tel: 00 353 1 601 7200

Galway (Furbo) – Connemara Coast Hotel, Furbo, Galway. Tel: 00 353 91 592108

Gorey (Co Wexford) – Marlfield House, Gorey, Co Wexford IRELAND. Tel: 00 353 55 21124

Kenmare – The Park Hotel Kenmare, Kenmare, Co Kerry. Tel: 00 353 64 41200

Kenmare (Co Kerry) – Sheen Falls Lodge, Kenmare, Co. Kerry. Tel: 00 353 64 41600

Killarney (Co Kerry) – Aghadoe Heights Hotel, Aghadoe, Killarney, Co Kerry. Tel: 00 353 64 31766

Killarney (Co Kerry) – Muckross Park Hotel, Muckross, Killarney, Co Kerry. Tel: 00 353 64 31938

Killarney (Co Kerry) – Randles Court Hotel, Muckross Road, Killarney, Co Kerry. Tel: 00 353 64 35333

Kiltegan (West Wicklow) – Humewood Castle, Kiltegan, Co Wicklow. Tel: 00 353 508 73215

Mallow (Co Cork) – Longueville House & Presidents' Restaurant, Mallow, Co Cork. Tel: 00 353 22 47156

Newmarket-On-Fergus (Co. Clare) – Dromoland Castle, Newmarket-On-Fergus, Co. Clare. Tel: 00 353 61 368144

Parknasilla – Parknasilla Hotel, Great Southern Hotel, Parknasilla, Co Kerry. Tel: 00 353 64 45122

Rathnew (Co Wicklow) – Hunter's Hotel, Rathnew, Co Wicklow. Tel: 00 353 404 40106

Rosslare (Co Wexford) – Kelly's Resort Hotel, Rosslare, Co Wexford. Tel: 00 353 53 32114

Rossnowlagh (Donegal) – The Sand House Hotel, Rossnowlagh, Donegal Bay, Co Donegal. Tel: 00 353 72 51777

CHANNEL ISLANDS

Guernsey (St Peter Port) – St Pierre Park Hotel, Rohais, St Peter Port, Guernsey GY1 1FD. Tel: 01481 728282

Jersey (Rozel) – Château La Chaire, Rozel Bay, Jersey JE3 6AJ. Tel: 01534 863354

Jersey (St Brelade) – The Atlantic Hotel, La Mont de la Pulente, St Brelade, Jersey JE3 8HE. Tel: 01534 744101

Jersey (St Brelade) – Hotel L'Horizon, St Brelade Bay, Jersey JE3 8EF. Tel: 01534 43101

Jersey (St Saviour) – Longueville Manor, St Saviour, Jersey JE2 7SA. Tel: 01534 725501

Johansens Recommended Traditional Inns, Hotels & Restaurants – Great Britain

ENGLAND

Aldbury (Ashridge N.T Estate) – The Greyhound Inn, Stocks Road, Aldbury, Near Tring, Hertfordshire HP23 5RT. Tel: 01442 851228

Aldeburgh – The Dolphin Inn, Thorpeness, Aldeburgh, Suffolk IP16 4NA. Tel: 01728 454994

Alfriston – Deans Place Hotel, Seaford Road, Alfriston, East Sussex BN26 5TW. Tel: 01323 870248

Amberley (Near Arundel) – The Boathouse Brasserie, Houghton Bridge, Amberley, Nr Arundel, West Sussex BN18 9LR. Tel: 01798 831059

Ambleside (Great Langdale) – The New Dungeon Ghyll Hotel, Great Langdale, Ambleside, Cumbria LA22 9JY. Tel: 015394 37213

Appleby-In-Westmorland – The Royal Oak Inn, Bongate, Appleby-In-Westmorland , Cumbria CA16 6UN. Tel: 017683 51463

Ashbourne (Hognaston) – Red Lion Inn, Main Street, Hognaston, Ashbourne, Derbyshire DE6 1PR. Tel: 01335 370396

Ashbourne (Waldley) – Beeches Country Restaurant, Waldley, Doveridge, Nr Ashbourne, Derbyshire DE6 5LR. Tel: 01889 590288

Badby Nr Daventry – The Windmill At Badby, Main Street, Badby, Nr Daventry, Northamptonshire NN11 6AN. Tel: 01327 702363

Bamburgh – The Victoria Hotel, Front Street, Bamburgh, Northumberland NE69 7BP. Tel: 01668 214431

Bassenthwaite Lake – The Pheasant, Bassenthwaite Lake, Nr Cockermouth, Cumbria CA13 9YE. Tel: 017687 76234

Beckington Nr Bath – The Woolpack Inn, Beckington, Nr Bath, Somerset BA3 6SP. Tel: 01373 831244

Belford – The Blue Bell Hotel, Market Place, Belford, Northumberland NE70 7NE. Tel: 01668 213543

Bibury – The Catherine Wheel, Bibury, Nr Cirencester, Gloucestershire GL7 5ND. Tel: 01285 740250

Bickleigh (Nr Tiverton) – The Fisherman's Cot, Bickleigh, Nr Tiverton, Devon EX16 8RW. Tel: 01884 855237 / 855289

Binfield – Stag & Hounds, Forest Road, Binfield, Berkshire RG12 9HA. Tel: 01344 483553

Blakeney – White Horse Hotel, 4 High Street, Blakeney, Holt, Norfolk NR25 7AL. Tel: 01263 740574

Bourton-On-The-Water – Dial House Hotel, The Chestnuts, High Street, Bourton-On-The-Water , Gloucestershire GL54 2AN. Tel: 01451 822244

Bridport (West Bexington) – The Manor Hotel, West Bexington, Dorchester, Dorset DT2 9DF. Tel: 01308 897616

Bristol – The New Inn, Badminton Road, Mayshill, Nr Frampton Cottrell, Bristol BS36 2NT. Tel: 01454 773161

Bristol (Aust) – The Boars Head, Main Road, Aust, Bristol BS12 3AX. Tel: 01454 632581

Broadway – The Broadway Hotel, The Green, Broadway, Worcestershire WR12 7AA. Tel: 01386 852401

Brockenhurst – The Snakecatcher, Lyndhurst, Brockenhurst, Hampshire SO42 7RL. Tel: 01590 622348

Burford – Cotswold Gateway Hotel, Cheltenham Road, Burford, Oxfordshire OX18 4HX. Tel: 01993 822695

Burford – The Golden Pheasant Hotel & Restaurant, The High Street, Burford, Oxford OX18 4QA. Tel: 01993 823417

Burford – The Lamb Inn, Sheep Street, Burford, Oxfordshire OX18 4LR. Tel: 01993 823155

Burford (The Barringtons) – The Inn For All Seasons, The Barringtons, Burford, Oxfordshire OX18 4TN. Tel: 01451 844324

Burnham Market – The Hoste Arms Hotel, The Green, Burnham Market, Norfolk PE31 8HD. Tel: 01328 738777

Burnley (Fence) – Fence Gate Inn, Wheatley Lane Road, Fence, Nr Burnley, Lancashire BB12 9EE. Tel: 01282 618101

Burnsall (Skipton) – The Red Lion, By the bridge at Burnsall, Near Skipton, North Yorkshire BD23 6BU. Tel: 01756 720204

Burton upon Trent – Ye Olde Dog & Partridge, High Street, Tutbury, Burton upon Trent, Staffordshire DE13 9LS. Tel: 01283 813030

Burton Upon Trent (Sudbury) – Boar's Head Hotel, Lichfield Road, Sudbury, Derbyshire DE6 5GX. Tel: 01283 820344

Calver (Near Bakewell) – The Chequers Inn, Froggatt Edge, Nr Calver, Derbyshire S30 1ZB. Tel: 01433 630231

Camborne – Tyacks Hotel, 27 Commercial Street, Camborne, Cornwall TR14 8LD. Tel: 01209 612424

Cambridge (Withersfield) – The White Horse Inn, Hollow Hill, Withersfield, Haverhill, Suffolk CB9 7SH. Tel: 01440 706081

Carlisle (Talkin Tarn) – The Tarn End House Hotel, Talkin Tarn, Brampton, Cumbria CA8 1LS. Tel: 016977 2340

Castle Ashby – The Falcon Hotel, Castle Ashby, Northampton, Northamptonshire NN7 1LF. Tel: 01604 696200

Chippenham – The Crown Inn, Giddea Hall, Yatton Keynell, Chippenham, Wiltshire SN14 7ER. Tel: 01249 782229

Chipping Sodbury – The Codrington Arms, Wapley Road, Codrington, Nr Chipping Sodbury, Bristol BS37 6RY. Tel: 01454 313145

Christchurch (Highcliffe on Sea) – The Lord Bute, 181 / 185 Lymington Road, Highcliffe on Sea, Christchurch , Dorset BH23 4JS. Tel: 01425 278884

Cirencester (Coln St-Aldwyns) – The New Inn at Coln, Coln St-Aldwyns, Nr Cirencester, Gloucestershire GL7 5AN. Tel: 01285 750651

Cirencester (South Cerney) – The Eliot Arms Hotel, Clarks Hay, South Cerney, Cirencester, Gloucestershire GL7 2UA. Tel: 01285 860215

Clare (Hundon) – The Plough Inn, Brockley Green, Sudbury, Nr Hundon, Suffolk CO10 8DT. Tel: 01440 786789

Clavering (Stansted) – The Cricketers, Clavering, Nr Saffron Walden, Essex CB11 4QT. Tel: 01799 550442

Cleobury Mortimer – Crown At Hopton, Hopton Wafers, Cleobury Mortimer, Shropshire DY14 0NB. Tel: 01299 270372

Cleobury Mortimer – The Redfern Hotel, Cleobury Mortimer, Shropshire DY14 8AA. Tel: 01299 270 395

Colchester (Coggeshall) – The White Hart Hotel & Restaurant, Market End, Coggeshall, Essex CO6 1NH. Tel: 01376 561654

Coleford – The New Inn, Coleford, Crediton, Devon EX17 5BZ. Tel: 01363 84242

Dartmouth – The Little Admiral Hotel, Victoria Road, Dartmouth, Devon TQ6 9RT. Tel: 01803 832572

Ditcheat (Nr Wells) – The Manor House Inn, Ditcheat, Somerset BA4 6RB. Tel: 01749 860276

Doncaster – Hamilton's Restaurant & Hotel, Carr House Road, Doncaster, South Yorkshire DN4 5HP. Tel: 01302 760770

Dorchester-On-Thames – The George Hotel, High Street, Dorchester-On-Thames, Oxford OX10 7HH. Tel: 01865 340404

East Witton (Wensleydale) – The Blue Lion, East Witton, Nr Leyburn, North Yorkshire DL8 4SN. Tel: 01969 624273

Eccleshall – The George Inn, Eccleshall, Staffordshire ST21 6DF. Tel: 01785 850300

Edenbridge – Ye Old Crown, High Street, Edenbridge, Kent TN8 5AR. Tel: 01732 867896

Egton (Nr Whitby) – The Wheatsheaf Inn, Egton, Nr Whitby, North Yorkshire YO21 1TZ. Tel: 01947 895271

Eton (Windsor) – The Christopher Hotel, High Street, Eton, Windsor, Berkshire SL4 6AN. Tel: 01753 811677 / 852359

Evershot – The Acorn Inn Hotel, Fore Street, Evershot, Nr Dorchester, Dorset DT2 0JW. Tel: 01935 83228

Evesham – The Northwick Hotel, Waterside, Evesham, Worcestershire WR11 6BT. Tel: 01386 40322

Evesham (Offenham) – Riverside Restaurant And Hotel, The Parks, Offenham Road, Nr Evesham, Worcestershire WR11 5JP. Tel: 01386 446200

Exmoor – The Royal Oak Inn, Winsford, Exmoor National Park, Somerset TA24 7JE. Tel: 01643 851455

Falmouth (Constantine) – Trengilly Wartha Country Inn & Restaurant, Nancenoy, Constantine, Falmouth, Cornwall TR11 5RP. Tel: 01326 340332

Fifield (Nr Burford) – The Merrymouth Inn, Stow Road, Fifield, Nr Burford, Oxford OX7 6HR. Tel: 01993 831652

Ford,Nr Bath – The White Hart, Ford, Chippenham, Wiltshire SN14 8RP. Tel: 01249 782213

Fordingbridge (New Forest) – The Woodfalls Inn, The Ridge, Woodfalls, Fordingbridge, Hampshire SP5 2LN. Tel: 01725 513222

Goring-On-Thames – The Leatherne Bottel Riverside Inn & Restaurant, The Bridleway, Goring-On-Thames, Berkshire RG8 0HS. Tel: 01491 872667

Grimsthorpe (Bourne) – The Black Horse Inn, Grimsthorpe, Bourne, Lincolnshire PE10 0LY. Tel: 01778 591247

Grindleford – The Maynard Arms, Main Road, Grindleford, Derbyshire S32 2HE. Tel: 01433 630321

Halifax/Huddersfield – The Rock Inn Hotel, Holywell Green, Halifax, West Yorkshire HX4 9BS. Tel: 01422 379721

Handcross (Slaugham) – The Chequers At Slaugham, Slaugham, Nr Handcross, West Sussex RH17 6AQ. Tel: 01444 400239/400996

Harrogate – The George & Olive's Restaurant, Wormald Green, Nr Harrogate, North Yorkshire HG3 3PR. Tel: 01765 677214

Harrogate (Killinghall) – The Low Hall Hotel, Ripon Road, Killinghall, Harrogate, North Yorkshire HG3 2AY. Tel: 01423 508598

Harrogate (Knaresborough) – The Dower House, Bond End, Knaresborough, Nr Harrogate, North Yorkshire HG5 9AL. Tel: 01423 863302

Harrogate (Ripley Castle) – The Boar's Head Hotel, Ripley, Harrogate, North Yorkshire HG3 3AY. Tel: 01423 771888

Hartley Wintney (Bramshill) – The Hatchgate, Bramshill, Nr Hook, Hampshire RG27 0JX. Tel: 01189 32666

Hathersage – The Plough Inn, Leadmill Bridge, Hathersage, Derbyshire S30 1BA. Tel: 01433 650319

Hay-On-Wye – Rhydspence Inn, Whitney-On-Wye, Nr Hay-On-Wye, Herefordshire HR3 6EU. Tel: 01497 831262

Hayfield (High Peak) – The Waltzing Weasel, New Mills Road, Birch Vale, High Peak, Derbyshire SK22 1BT. Tel: 01663 743402

Helmsley – The Feathers Hotel, Market Place, Helmsley, North Yorkshire YO6 5BH. Tel: 01439 770275

Helmsley (Near York) – The Feversham Arms Hotel, Helmsley , North Yorkshire YO6 5AG. Tel: 01439 770766

Hindon (Nr Salisbury) – The Grosvenor Arms, Hindon, Salisbury, Wiltshire SP3 6DJ. Tel: 01747 820696

Hindon, Nr Salisbury – The Lamb at Hindon, High Street, Hindon, Salisbury, Wiltshire SP3 6DP. Tel: 01747 820573

Honiton (Wilmington) – Home Farm Hotel, Wilmington, Nr Honiton, Devon EX14 9JR. Tel: 01404 831278

Huddersfield (Golcar) – The Weavers Shed Restaurant with Rooms, Knowl Road, Golcar, Huddersfield, West Yorkshire HD7 4AN. Tel: 01484 654284

Ilchester – Northover Manor, Ilchester, Somerset BA22 8LD. Tel: 01935 840447

Kenilworth – Clarendon House Bar Brasserie Hotel, High Street, Kenilworth, Warwickshire CV8 1LZ. Tel: 01926 857668

Kingskerswell (Nr Torquay) – The Barn Owl Inn, Aller Mills, Kingskerswell, Devon TQ12 5AN. Tel: 01803 872130

Knutsford – Longview Hotel And Restaurant, 51/55 Manchester Road, Knutsford, Cheshire WA16 0LX. Tel: 01565 632119

Ledbury – Feathers Hotel, High Street, Ledbury, Herefordshire HR8 1DS. Tel: 01531 635266

Leek (Blackshaw Moor) – The Three Horseshoes Inn & Kirk's Restaurant, Buxton Road, Blackshaw Moor, Nr Leek, Staffordshire ST13 8TW. Tel: 01538 300296

Long Melford – The Countrymen, The Green, Long Melford, Suffolk CO10 9DN. Tel: 01787 312356

Longleat (Horningsham) – The Bath Arms, Horningsham, Warminster, Wiltshire BA12 7LY. Tel: 01985 844308

Lymington – The Angel Inn, High Street, New Forest, Hampshire SO41 9AP. Tel: 01590 672050

Lynmouth – The Rising Sun, Harbourside, Lynmouth, Devon EX35 6EQ. Tel: 01598 753223

Maidstone (Ringlestone) – Ringlestone Inn, 'Twixt Harrietsham and Wormshill, Nr Maidstone, Kent ME17 1NX. Tel: 01622 859900

Malmesbury – The Horse And Groom Inn, Charlton, Near Malmesbury, Wiltshire SN16 9DL. Tel: 01666 823904

Mells (Nr Bath) – The Talbot Inn at Mells, Selwood Street, Mells, Nr Bath, Somerset BA11 3PN. Tel: 01373 812254

Newbury (Gt Shefford) – The Swan Inn, Newbury Road, Great Shefford, Newbury, Berkshire RG17 7DS. Tel: 01488 648271

Newby Bridge – The Swan Hotel, Newby Bridge, Nr Ulverston, Cumbria LA12 8NB. Tel: 015395 31681

North Walsham – Elderton Lodge, Gunton Park, Thorpe Market, Nr North Walsham, Norfolk NR11 8TZ. Tel: 01263 833547

Nottingham – Hotel Des Clos, Old Lenton Lane, Nottingham, Nottinghamshire NG7 2SA. Tel: 01159 866566

Old Hunstanton – The Lodge Hotel & Restaurant, Old Hunstanton, Norfolk PE36 6HX. Tel: 01485 532896

Oxford (Banbury) – Holcombe Hotel, High Street, Deddington, Nr Woodstock, Oxfordshire OX15 0SL. Tel: 01869 338274

Oxford (Middleton Stoney) – The Jersey Arms, Middleton Stoney, Oxfordshire OX6 8SE. Tel: 01869 343234

Oxford (Minster Lovell) – The Mill & Old Swan, Minster Lovell, Nr Burford, Oxfordshire OX8 5RN. Tel: 01993 774441

Pelynt,Nr Looe – Jubilee Inn, Pelynt, Nr Looe, Cornwall PL13 2JZ. Tel: 01503 220312

Penistone (Ingbirchworth) – The Fountain Inn & Rooms, Wellthorne Lane, Ingbirchworth, Nr Penistone, South Yorkshire S36 7GJ. Tel: 01226 763125

Petworth – The Stonemason's Inn, North Street, Petworth, West Sussex GU28 9NL. Tel: 01798 342510

Petworth (Coultershaw Bridge) – Badgers, Coultershaw Bridge, Petworth, West Sussex GU28 0JF. Tel: 01798 342651

Petworth (Fittleworth) – The Swan Inn, Lower Street, Fittleworth, Nr Petworth, West Sussex RH20 1EN. Tel: 01798 865429

Petworth (Sutton) – White Horse Inn, Sutton, Nr Pulborough, West Sussex RH20 1PS. Tel: 01798 869 221

Port Gaverne – The Port Gaverne Inn, Nr Port Isaac, North Cornwall PL29 3SQ. Tel: 01208 880244

Preston (Goosnargh) – Ye Horn's Inn, Horn's Lane, Goosnargh, Nr Preston, Lancashire PR3 2FJ. Tel: 01772 865230

Reading (Streatley) – The Bull at Streatley, Reading Road, Reading, Berkshire RG8 9TJ. Tel: 01491 875231

Romsey (Greatbridge) – Duke's Head, Greatbridge, Nr Romsey, Hampshire SO51 0HB. Tel: 01794 514450

Rugby (Easenhall) – The Golden Lion Inn of Easenhall, Easenhall, Nr Rugby, Warwickshire CV23 0JA. Tel: 01788 832265

Rye – The George Hotel, High Street, Rye, East Sussex TN31 7JP. Tel: 01797 222114

Saddleworth (Delph) – The Old Bell Inn Hotel, Huddersfield Road, Delph, Saddleworth, Nr Oldham, Greater Manchester OL3 5EG. Tel: 01457 870130

Salisbury (Downton) – The White Horse, Downton, Salisbury, Wiltshire SP5 3LY. Tel: 01725 510408

Sheffield (Dronfield) – Manor House Hotel & Restaurant, High Street, Old Dronfield, Derbyshire S18 1PY. Tel: 01246 413971

Sherborne – The Half Moon Inn, Half Moon Street, Sherborne, Dorset DT9 3LN. Tel: 01935 812017

Sherborne (Oborne) – The Grange Hotel & Restaurant, Oborne, Nr Sherborne, Dorset DT9 4LA. Tel: 01935 813463

Sherborne (West Camel) – The Walnut Tree, West Camel, Nr Sherborne, Somerset BA22 7QW. Tel: 01935 851292

Shifnal (Telford) – Naughty Nell's, 1 Park Street, Shifnal, Shropshire TF11 9BA. Tel: 01952 411412

Shipton Under Wychwood – The Shaven Crown Hotel, High Street, Shipton Under Wychwood, Oxfordshire OX7 6BA. Tel: 01993 830330

Snettisham (Nr King's Lynn) – The Rose & Crown, Old Church Road, Snettisham, King's Lynn, Norfolk PE31 7LX. Tel: 01485 541382

Southport (Formby) – Tree Tops Country House Restaurant & Hotel, Southport Old Road, Formby, Nr Southport, Lancashire L37 0AB. Tel: 01704 572430

Stafford (Ingestre) – The Dower House, Ingestre Park, Great Haywood, Staffordshire ST18 0RE. Tel: 01889 270707

Stamford – The Crown Hotel, All Saints Place, Stamford, Lincolnshire PE9 2AG. Tel: 01780 763136

Stamford (Nr Grantham) – Black Bull Inn, Lobthorpe, Nr Grantham, Lincolnshire NG33 5LL. Tel: 01476 860086

Stow-on-the-Wold – The Unicorn Hotel, Sheep Street, Stow-on-the-Wold, Gloucestershire GL54 1HQ. Tel: 01451 830257

Stow-On-The-Wold (Bledington) – The Kings Head Inn & Restaurant, The Green, Bledington, Oxfordshire OX7 6XQ. Tel: 01608 658365

Stratford-upon-Avon – The Coach House Hotel & Cellar Restaurant, 16/17 Warwick Road, Stratford-upon-Avon, Warwickshire CV37 6YW. Tel: 01789 204109 / 299468

Stroud (Frampton Mansell) – The Crown Inn, Frampton Mansell, Stroud, Gloucestershire GL6 8JG. Tel: 01285 760601

Sudbury (Long Melford) – The Bull Hotel, Hall Street, Long Melford, Suffolk CO10 9JG. Tel: 01787 378494

Taunton (Staple Fitzpaine) – Greyhound Inn, Staple Fitzpaine, Nr Taunton, Somerset TA3 5SP. Tel: 01823 480227

Telford (Hadley Park) – Hadley Park House Hotel, Hadley Park, Telford, Shropshire TF1 4UL. Tel: 01952 677269

Telford (Norton) – The Hundred House Hotel, Bridgnorth Road,Norton, Nr Shifnal, Telford, Shropshire TF11 9EE. Tel: 01952 730353

Tenterden – The White Lion Hotel, The High Street, Tenterden, Kent TN30 6BD. Tel: 01580 765077

Thaxted – Recorders House Restaurant (With Rooms), 17 Town Street, Thaxted, Essex CM6 2LD. Tel: 01371 830438

Thirsk – Crab & Lobster, Asenby, North Yorkshire YO7 3QL. Tel: 01845 577286

Thornham – The Lifeboat Inn, Ship Lane, Thornham, Norfolk PE36 6LT. Tel: 01485 512236

Thorpe Market – Green Farm Restaurant And Hotel, North Walsham Road, Thorpe Market, Norfolk NR11 8TH. Tel: 01263 833602

Tintagel (Trebarwith Strand) – The Port William, Trebarwith Strand, Nr Tintagel, Cornwall PL34 0HB. Tel: 01840 770230

Totnes (Bow Bridge, Ashprington) – The Watermans Arms, Bow Bridge, Ashprington, Nr Totnes, Devon TQ9 7EG. Tel: 01803 732214

Totnes (Staverton) – The Sea Trout Inn, Staverton, Nr Totnes, Devon TQ9 6PA. Tel: 01803 762274

Troutbeck (Near Windermere) – The Mortal Man Hotel, Troutbeck, Nr Windermere, Cumbria LA23 1PL. Tel: 015394 33193

Upton-Upon-Severn,Nr Malvern – The White Lion Hotel, High Street, Upton-Upon-Severn, Nr Malvern, Worcestershire WR8 0HJ. Tel: 01684 592551

Warminster (Upton Scudamore) – The Angel Inn, Upton Scudamore, Warminster, Wiltshire BA12 0AG. Tel: 01985 213225

Wells – The Market Place Hotel, Wells, Somerset BA5 2RW. Tel: 01749 672616

Weobley – The Salutation Inn, Market Pitch, Weobley, Herefordshire HR4 8SJ. Tel: 01544 318443

West Auckland – The Manor House Hotel & Country Club, The Green, West Auckland, County Durham DL14 9HW. Tel: 01388 834834

West Witton (Wensleydale) – The Wensleydale Heifer Inn, West Witton, Wensleydale, North Yorkshire DL8 4LS. Tel: 01969 622322

Whitewell – The Inn At Whitewell, Forest Of Bowland, Clitheroe, Lancashire BB7 3AT. Tel: 01200 448222

Witney (Hailey) – The Bird in Hand, Hailey, Witney, Oxfordshire OX8 5XP. Tel: 01993 868321

Wooler – The Tankerville Arms Hotel, Wooler, Northumberland NE71 6AD. Tel: 01668 281581

Worthing (Bramber) – The Old Tollgate Restaurant And Hotel, The Street, Bramber, Steyning, West Sussex BN44 3WE. Tel: 01903 879494

Wroxham – The Barton Angler Country Inn, Irstead Road, Neatishead, Nr Wroxham, Norfolk NR12 8XP. Tel: 01692 630740

York (Easingwold) – The George at Easingwold, Market Place, Easingwold, York, North Yorkshire YO6 3AD. Tel: 01347 821698

WALES

Chepstow – The Castle View Hotel, 16 Bridge Street, Chepstow, Monmouthshire NP6 5EZ. Tel: 01291 620349

Llanarmon Dyffryn Ceiriog – The West Arms Hotel, Llanarmon D C, Nr Llangollen, Denbighshire LL20 7LD. Tel: 01691 600665

Llandeilo (Rhosmaen) – The Plough Inn, Rhosmaen, Llandeilo, Carmarthenshire SA19 6NP. Tel: 01558 823431

Machynlleth – The Wynnstay, Maengwyn Street, Machynlleth, Powys SY20 8AE. Tel: 01654 702941

Presteigne – The Radnorshire Arms, High Street, Presteigne, Powys. Tel: 01544 267406

SCOTLAND

Glendevon (South Perthshire) – Tormaukin Hotel, Glendevon, By Dollar, Perthshire FK14 7JY. Tel: 01259 781252

Inverness (Farr) – Grouse & Trout, Flichity, By Farr, Inverness, IV2 6X5. Tel: 01808 521314

Isle Of Skye (Eilean Iarmain) – Hotel Eilean Iarmain, Sleat, Isle Of Skye IV43 8QR. Tel: 01471 833332

Isle Of Skye (Uig) – Uig Hotel, Uig, Isle Of Skye, Isle Of Skye IV51 9YE. Tel: 01470 542205

Kylesku (Sutherland) – Kylesku Hotel, Kylesku, Via Lairg, Sutherland IV27 4HW. Tel: 01971 502231/502200

Loch Earn (Perthshire) – Achray House on Loch Earn, Loch Earn, St Fillan, Perthshire PH6 2NF. Tel: 01764 685231

Moffat – Annandale Arms Hotel, High Street, Moffat, Dumfriesshire DG10 9HF. Tel: 01683 220013

Pitlochry – The Moulin Hotel, Moulin, By Pitlochry, Perthshire PH16 5EW. Tel: 01796 472196

Plockton (By Kyle of Lochalsh) – The Plockton Hotel & Garden Restaurant, Harbour Street, Plockton, Wester Ross IV52 8TN. Tel: 01599 544274

Poolewe (Wester Ross) – Pool House Hotel, Poolewe, Achnasheen, Wester Ross IV22 2LD. Tel: 01445 781272

CHANNEL ISLANDS

Guernsey (St Peter Port) – Les Rocquettes Hotel, Les Gravees, St Peter Port, GY1 1RN. Tel: 01481 722176

Johansens Recommended Country Houses & Small Hotels – Great Britain & Ireland

ENGLAND

Alcester (Arrow) – Arrow Mill Hotel And Restaurant, Arrow, Nr Alcester, Warwickshire B49 5NL. Tel: 01789 762419

Ambleside (Clappersgate) – Nanny Brow Country House Hotel & Restaurant, Clappersgate, Ambleside, Cumbria LA22 9NF. Tel: 015394 32036

Ampleforth – Shallowdale House, Ampleforth, York, North Yorkshire YO62 4DY. Tel: 01439 788325

Appleton-Le-Moors – Appleton Hall, Appleton-Le-Moors, North Yorkshire YO62 6TF. Tel: 01751 417227

Arundel (Burpham) – Burpham Country House Hotel, Old Down, Burpham, Nr Arundel, West Sussex BN18 9RJ. Tel: 01903 882160

Atherstone – Chapel House, Friars' Gate, Atherstone, Warwickshire CV9 1EY. Tel: 01827 718949

Bakewell (Rowsley) – East Lodge Country House Hotel, Rowsley, Matlock, Derbyshire DE4 2EF. Tel: 01629 734474

Bakewell (Rowsley) – The Peacock Hotel at Rowsley, Rowsley, Near Matlock, Derbyshire DE4 2EB. Tel: 01629 733518

Bamburgh – Waren House Hotel, Waren Mill, Bamburgh, Northumberland NE70 7EE. Tel: 01668 214581

Barnstaple (Bishops Tawton) – Downrew House Hotel, Bishops Tawton, Barnstaple, Devon EX32 0DY. Tel: 01271 342497

Bath – Apsley House, 141 Newbridge Hill, Bath, Somerset BA1 3PT. Tel: 01225 336966

Bath – Bloomfield House, 146 Bloomfield Road, Bath, Somerset BA2 2AS. Tel: 01225 420105

Bath – Dukes' Hotel, Great Pulteney Street, Bath, Somerset BA2 4DN. Tel: 01225 463512

Bath – Eagle House, Church Street, Bathford, Somerset BA1 7RS. Tel: 01225 859946

Bath – Oldfields, 102 Wells Road, Bath, Somerset BA2 3AL. Tel: 01225 317984

Bath – Paradise House, Holloway, Bath, Somerset BA2 4PX. Tel: 01225 317723

Bath – Villa Magdala, Henrietta Road, Bath, Somerset BA2 6LX. Tel: 01225 466329

Bath (Bradford-On-Avon) – Widbrook Grange, Trowbridge Road, Bradford-On-Avon, Wiltshire BA15 1UH. Tel: 01225 864750 / 863173

Bath (Midsomer Norton) – The Old Priory Hotel, Church Square, Midsomer Norton, Bath, Somerset BA3 2HX. Tel: 01761 416784

Bath (Norton St Philip) – Bath Lodge Hotel, Norton St Philip, Bath, Somerset BA3 6NH. Tel: 01225 723040

Bath (Woolverton) – Woolverton House, Woolverton, Nr Bath, Somerset BA3 6QS. Tel: 01373 830415

Belper (Shottle) – Dannah Farm Country House, Bowman's Lane, Shottle, Nr Belper, Derbyshire DE56 2DR. Tel: 01773 550273 / 630

Beverley (Walkington) – The Manor House, Northlands, Walkington, East Yorkshire HU17 8RT. Tel: 01482 881645

Bibury – Bibury Court, Bibury , Gloucestershire GL7 5NT. Tel: 01285 740337

Bicester (Chesterton) – Bignell Park Hotel, Chesterton, Nr Bicester, OX6 8UE. Tel: 01869 241444

Bideford (Northam) – Yeoldon House Hotel, Durrant Lane, Northam, Nr Bideford, Devon EX39 2RL. Tel: 01237 474400

Biggin-By-Hartington – Biggin Hall, Biggin-By-Hartington, Buxton, Derbyshire SK17 0DH. Tel: 01298 84451

Blockley (Chipping Campden) – Lower Brook House, Blockley, Nr Moreton-In-Marsh, Gloucestershire GL56 9DS. Tel: 01386 700286

Bolton (Edgworth) – Pelton Fold Farm, Bury Road, Edgworth, Bolton, Lancashire BL7 0BS. Tel: 01204 852207

Bolton (Edgworth) – Quarlton Manor Farm, Plantation Road , Edgeworth,Turton, Bolton , Lancashire BL7 0DD. Tel: 01204 852277

Bridgnorth – Cross Lane House Hotel, Cross Lane Head, Bridgnorth, Shropshire WV16 4SJ. Tel: 01746 764887

Brighton – The Granville, 124 Kings Road, Brighton, East Sussex BN1 2FA. Tel: 01273 326302

Broadway – The Broadway Hotel, The Green, Broadway, Worcestershire WR12 7AA. Tel: 01386 852401

Broadway – Collin House Hotel, Collin Lane, Broadway, Worcestershire WR12 7PB. Tel: 01386 858354

Broadway (Willersey) – The Old Rectory, Church Street, Willersey, Broadway, Gloucestershire WR12 7PN. Tel: 01386 853729

Brockenhurst – Thatched Cottage Hotel & Restaurant, 16 Brookley Road, Brockenhurst, New Forest, Hampshire SO42 7RR. Tel: 01590 623090

Brockenhurst – Whitley Ridge & Country House Hotel, Beaulieu Road, Brockenhurst, New Forest, Hampshire SO42 7QL. Tel: 01590 622354

Buttermere (Lorton Vale) – New House Farm, Lorton, Cockermouth, Cumbria CA13 9UU. Tel: 01900 85404

Cambridge (Melbourn) – Melbourn Bury, Melbourn, Cambridgeshire, Nr Royston, Cambridgeshire SG8 6DE. Tel: 01763 261151

Carlisle (Crosby-On-Eden) – Crosby Lodge Country House Hotel, High Crosby, Crosby-On-Eden, Carlisle, Cumbria CA6 4QZ. Tel: 01228 573618

Cartmel – Aynsome Manor Hotel, Cartmel, Grange-Over-Sands, Cumbria LA11 6HH. Tel: 015395 36653

Castle Cary – Bond's - Bistro with Rooms, Ansford Hill, Castle Cary, Somerset BA7 7JP. Tel: 01963 350464

Chagford – Easton Court Hotel, Easton Cross, Chagford, Devon TQ13 8JL. Tel: 01647 433469

Chagford – Mill End Hotel, Dartmoor National Park, Chagford, Devon TQ13 8JN. Tel: 01647 432282

Cheltenham (Charlton Kings) – Charlton Kings Hotel, Charlton Kings, Cheltenham, Gloucestershire GL52 6UU. Tel: 01242 231061

Cheltenham (Withington) – Halewell, Halewell Close, Withington, Nr Cheltenham, Gloucestershire GL54 4BN. Tel: 01242 890238

Chester – Green Bough Hotel, 60 Hoole Road, Chester, Cheshire CH2 3NL. Tel: 01244 326241

Chichester (Apuldram) – Crouchers Bottom Country Hotel, Birdham Road, Apuldram, Nr Chichester, West Sussex PO20 7EH. Tel: 01243 784995

Chichester (Charlton) – Woodstock House Hotel, Charlton, Nr Chichester, West Sussex PO18 0HU. Tel: 01243 811666

Chippenham – Stanton Manor, Stanton Saint Quinton, Nr Chippenham, Wiltshire SN14 6DQ. Tel: 01666 837552

Chipping Campden (Broad Campden) – The Malt House, Broad Campden, Gloucestershire GL55 6UU. Tel: 01386 840295

Church Stretton (Little Stretton) – Mynd House Hotel & Restaurant, Little Stretton, Church Stretton, Nr Shrewsbury, Shropshire SY6 6RB. Tel: 01694 722212

Clearwell – Tudor Farmhouse Hotel & Restaurant, High Street, Clearwell, Nr Coleford, Gloucestershire GL16 8JS. Tel: 01594 833046

Clovelly (Horns Cross) – Foxdown Manor, Horns Cross, Clovelly, Devon EX39 5PJ. Tel: 01237 451325

Coalville (Greenhill) – Abbots Oak, Greenhill, Coalville, Leicestershire LE67 4UY. Tel: 01530 832 328

Combe Martin (East Down) – Ashelford, Ashelford, East Down, Nr Barnstaple, Devon EX31 4LU. Tel: 01271 850469

Crediton (Coleford) – Coombe House Country Hotel, Coleford, Crediton, Devon EX17 5BY. Tel: 01363 84487

Dartmoor (Haytor Vale) – Bel Alp House, Haytor , Nr Bovey Tracey, Devon TQ13 9XX. Tel: 01364 661217

Diss (Fressingfield) – Chippenhall Hall, Fressingfield, Eye, Suffolk IP21 5TD. Tel: 01379 588180 / 586733

Diss (Starston) – Starston Hall, Starston, Harleston, Norfolk IP20 9PU. Tel: 01379 854252

Doncaster – Hamilton's Restaurant & Hotel, Carr House Road, Doncaster, South Yorkshire DN4 5HP. Tel: 01302 760770

Dorchester (Lower Bockhampton) – Yalbury Cottage Hotel, Lower Bockhampton, Dorchester, Dorset DT2 8PZ. Tel: 01305 262382

Dorchester-On-Thames – The George Hotel, High Street, Dorchester-On-Thames, Oxford OX10 7HH. Tel: 01865 340404

Dover (Temple Ewell) – The Woodville Hall, Temple Ewell, Dover , Kent CT16 3DJ. Tel: 01304 825256

Dover (West Cliffe) – Wallett's Court, West Cliffe, St. Margaret's-at-Cliffe, Nr Dover, Kent CT15 6EW. Tel: 01304 852424

Dulverton – Ashwick Country House Hotel, Dulverton, Somerset TA22 9QD. Tel: 01398 323868

Enfield (London) – Oak Lodge Hotel, 80 Village Road, Bush Hill Park, Enfield, Middlesex EN1 2EU. Tel: 020 8360 7082

Epsom – Chalk Lane Hotel, Chalk Lane, Epsom, Surrey KT18 7BB. Tel: 01372 721179

Evershot – Rectory House, Fore Street, Evershot, Dorset DT2 0JW. Tel: 0193583 273

Evesham (Harvington) – The Mill At Harvington, Anchor Lane, Harvington, Evesham, Worcestershire WR11 5NR. Tel: 01386 870688

Exford (Exmoor) – The Crown Hotel, Exford , Exmoor National Park, Somerset TA24 7PP. Tel: 01643 831554/5

Exmoor (Minehead) – The Beacon Country House Hotel, Beacon Road, Minehead, Somerset TA24 5SD. Tel: 01643 703476

Falmouth (Mawnan Smith) – Trelawne Hotel-The Hutches Restaurant, Mawnan Smith, Nr Falmouth, Cornwall TR11 5HS. Tel: 01326 250226

Fenny Drayton (Nr Nuneaton) – White Wings, Quaker Close, Fenny Drayton, Nr Nuneaton, Leicestershire CV13 6BS. Tel: 01827 716100

Gatwick (Charlwood) – Stanhill Court Hotel, Stan Hill , Charlwood, Nr Horley, Surrey RH6 0EP. Tel: 01293 862166

Golant by Fowey – The Cormorant Hotel, Golant, Fowey, Cornwall PL23 1LL. Tel: 01726 833426

Grasmere (Rydal Water) – White Moss House, Rydal Water, Grasmere, Cumbria LA22 9SE. Tel: 015394 35295

Great Snoring – The Old Rectory, Barsham Road, Great Snoring, Norfolk NR21 0HP. Tel: 01328 820597

Hampton Court (Hampton Wick) – Chase Lodge, 10 Park Road, Hampton Wick, Kingston Upon Thames, Surrey KT1 4AS. Tel: 020 8943 1862

Hamsterley Forest (Near Durham) – Grove House, Hamsterley Forest, Nr Bishop Auckland, Co.Durham DL13 3NL. Tel: 01388 488203

Harrogate – The White House, 10 Park Parade, Harrogate, North Yorkshire HG1 5AH. Tel: 01423 501388

Hawes (Wensleydale) – Rookhurst Country House Hotel, West End, Gayle, Hawes, North Yorkshire DL8 3RT. Tel: 01969 667454

Hawkshead (Near Sawrey) – Sawrey House Country Hotel, Near Sawrey, Hawkshead, Ambleside, Cumbria LA22 OLF. Tel: 015394 36387

Helston – Nansloe Manor, Meneage Road, Helston, Cornwall TR13 0SB. Tel: 01326 574691

Hereford (Fownhope) – The Bowens Country House, Fownhope, Herefordshire HR1 4PS. Tel: 01432 860430

Hereford (Ullingswick) – The Steppes, Ullingswick, Nr Hereford, Herefordshire HR1 3JG. Tel: 01432 820424

Holt (Felbrigg) – Felbrigg Lodge, Aylmerton, Norfolk NR11 8RA. Tel: 01263 837588

Ilminster (Cricket Malherbie) – The Old Rectory, Cricket Malherbie, Ilminster, Somerset TA19 0PW. Tel: 01460 54364

Ilsington (Dartmoor) – Ilsington Country Hotel, Ilsington, Newton Abbot, Devon TQ13 9RR. Tel: 01364 661452

Isle of Wight (Shanklin) – Rylstone Manor, Rylstone Gardens, Shanklin, Isle of Wight PO37 6RG. Tel: 01983 862806

Keswick (LakeThirlmere) – Dale Head Hall Lakeside Hotel, Thirlmere, Keswick, Cumbria CA12 4TN. Tel: 017687 72478

Keswick (Newlands) – Swinside Lodge Hotel, Grange Road, Newlands, Keswick, Cumbria CA12 5UE. Tel: 017687 72948

Kirkby Lonsdale – Hipping Hall, Cowan Bridge, Kirkby Lonsdale, Cumbria LA6 2JJ. Tel: 015242 71187

Lavenham – Lavenham Priory, Water Street, Lavenham, Sudbury, Suffolk CO10 9RW. Tel: 01787 247404

Leominster – Lower Bache House, Kimbolton, Nr Leominster, Herefordshire HR6 0ER. Tel: 01568 750304

Lifton (Sprytown) – The Thatched Cottage Country Hotel And Restaurant, Sprytown, Lifton, Devon PL16 0AY. Tel: 01566 784224

Lincoln (Washingborough) – Washingborough Hall, Church Hill, Washingborough, Lincoln, Lincolnshire LN4 1BE. Tel: 01522 790340

Looe (Widegates) – Coombe Farm, Widegates, Looe, Cornwall PL13 1QN. Tel: 01503 240223

Lorton – Winder Hall, Low Lorton, Nr Cockermouth, Cumbria CA13 9UP. Tel: 01900 85107

Loughborough – The Old Manor Hotel, 11-14 Sparrow Hill, Loughborough, Leicestershire LE11 1BT. Tel: 01509 211228

Ludlow (Diddlebury) – Delbury Hall, Diddlebury, Craven Arms, Shropshire SY7 9DH. Tel: 01584 841267

Ludlow (Overton) – Overton Grange Hotel, Overton, Ludlow, Shropshire SY8 4AD. Tel: 01584 873500

Luton (Little Offley) – Little Offley, Hitchin, Hertfordshire SG5 3BU. Tel: 01462 768243

Lydford (Vale Down) – Moor View House, Vale Down, Lydford, Devon EX20 4BB. Tel: 01822 820220

Lyme Regis (Charmouth) – Thatch Lodge Hotel, The Street, Charmouth, Nr Lyme Regis, Dorset DT6 6PQ. Tel: 01297 560407

Lymington – Rosefield House, Sway Road, Lymington, New Forest, Hampshire SO41 8LR. Tel: 01590 671526

Lymington (Hordle) – Hotel Gordleton Mill, Silver Street, Hordle, Nr Lymington, Hampshire SO41 6DJ. Tel: 01590 682219

Lynton – Hewitt's Hotel, North Walk, Lynton, Devon EX35 6HJ. Tel: 01598 752293

Maidstone (Boughton Monchelsea) – Tanyard, Wierton Hill, Boughton Monchelsea, Nr Maidstone, Kent ME17 4JT. Tel: 01622 744705

Malton – Newstead Grange, Norton-On-Derwent, Malton, North Yorkshire YO17 9PJ. Tel: 01653 692502

Maxey (Nr Stamford) – Abbey House & Coach House, West End Road, Maxey, Cambridge PE6 9EJ. Tel: 01778 344642

Middlecombe (Minehead) – Periton Park Hotel, Middlecombe, Nr Minehead, Somerset TA24 8SN. Tel: 01643 706885

Middleham (Wensleydale) – Millers House Hotel, Middleham, Wensleydale, North Yorkshire DL8 4NR. Tel: 01969 622630

Middleham (Wensleydale) – Waterford House, 19 Kirkgate, Middleham, North Yorkshire DL8 4PG. Tel: 01969 622090

Minchinhampton – Burleigh Court, Minchinhampton, Gloucestershire GL5 2PF. Tel: 01453 883804

Morchard Bishop – Wigham, Morchard Bishop, Crediton, Devon EX17 6RJ. Tel: 01363 877350

New Romney (Littlestone) – Romney Bay House, Coast Road, Littlestone, New Romney, Kent TN28 8QY. Tel: 01797 364747

North Walsham – Beechwood Hotel, Cromer Road, North Walsham, Norfolk NR28 0HD. Tel: 01692 403231

Norwich – The Beeches Hotel & Victorian Gardens, 2-6 Earlham Road, Norwich, Norfolk NR2 3DB. Tel: 01603 621167

Norwich (Coltishall) – Norfolk Mead Hotel, Coltishall, Norwich, Norfolk NR12 7DN. Tel: 01603 737531

Norwich (Drayton) – The Stower Grange, School Road, Drayton, Norfolk NR8 6EF. Tel: 01603 860210

Norwich (Old Catton) – Catton Old Hall, Lodge Lane, Catton, Norwich, Norfolk NR6 7HG. Tel: 01603 419379

Norwich (Thorpe St Andrew) – The Old Rectory, 103 Yarmouth Road, Thorpe St Andrew, Norwich, Norfolk NR7 0HF. Tel: 01603 700772

Nottingham – Cockliffe Country House Hotel, Nottingham, Nottinghamshire NG5 8PQ. Tel: 01159 680179

Nottingham (Langar) – Langar Hall, Langar, Nottinghamshire NG13 9HG. Tel: 01949 860559

Nottingham (Redmile) – L'Auberge, 29 Main Street, Redmile, Nottinghamshire NG13 0GA. Tel: 01949 843086

Nottingham (Ruddington) – The Cottage Country House Hotel, Easthorpe Street, Ruddington, Nottingham, Nottinghamshire NG11 6LA. Tel: 01159 846882

Ockham – The Hautboy, Ockham Lane, Ockham, Surrey GU23 6. Tel: 01483 225355

Oswestry – Pen-y-Dyffryn Country Hotel, Rhydycroesau, Nr Oswestry, Shropshire SY10 7JD. Tel: 01691 653700

Otterburn – The Tower, Otterburn, Northumberland NE19 1NS. Tel: 01830 520620

Owlpen – Owlpen Manor, Near Uley, Gloucestershire GL11 5BZ. Tel: 01453 860261

Oxford (Kingston Bagpuize) – Fallowfields, Kingston Bagpuize With Southmoor, Oxfordshire OX13 5BH. Tel: 01865 820416

Padstow – Cross House Hotel, Church Street, Padstow, Cornwall PL28 8BG. Tel: 01841 532391

Penrith (Temple Sowerby) – Temple Sowerby House Hotel, Temple Sowerby, Penrith, Cumbria CA10 1RZ. Tel: 017683 61578

Penzance – The Summer House, Cornwall Terrace, Penzance, Cornwall TR18 4HL. Tel: 01736 363744

Petersfield (Langrish) – Langrish House, Langrish, Nr Petersfield, Hampshire GU32 1RN. Tel: 01730 266941

Petworth – The Old Railway Station, Coultershaw Bridge, Petworth, West Sussex GU28 0JF. Tel: 01798 342346

Porlock Weir – The Cottage Hotel, Porlock Weir, Porlock, Somerset TA24 8PB. Tel: 01643 863300

Porlock Weir – Porlock Vale House, Porlock Weir, Somerset TA24 8NY. Tel: 01643 862338

Porthleven (Nr Helston) – Tye Rock Country House Hotel, Loe Bar Road, Porthleven, Nr Helston, Cornwall TR13 9EW. Tel: 01326 572695

Portsmouth – The Beaufort Hotel, 71 Festing Road, Portsmouth, Hampshire PO4 0NQ. Tel: 023 92823707

Preston (Gardstang) – Pickering Park Country House, Gardstang Road, Catterall, Gardstang, Lancashire PR3 0HD. Tel: 01995 600999

Pulborough – Chequers Hotel, Church Place, Pulborough, West Sussex RH20 1AD. Tel: 01798 872486

Ringwood – Moortown Lodge, 244 Christchurch Road, Ringwood, Hampshire BH24 3AS. Tel: 01425 471404

Ross-On-Wye (Glewstone) – Glewstone Court, Nr Ross-On-Wye, Herefordshire HR9 6AW. Tel: 01989 770367

Rye – White Vine House, High Street, Rye, East Sussex TN31 7JF. Tel: 01797 224748

Saham Toney (Thetford) – Broom Hall, Richmond Road, Saham Toney, Thetford, Norfolk IP25 7EX. Tel: 01953 882125

Saunton – Preston House Hotel, Saunton, Braunton, Devon EX33 1LG. Tel: 01271 890472

Seavington St Mary, Nr Ilminster – The Pheasant Hotel, Seavington St Mary, Nr Ilminster, Somerset TA19 0HQ. Tel: 01460 240502

Sherborne – The Eastbury Hotel, Long Street, Sherborne, Dorset DT9 3BY. Tel: 01935 813131

Shipton-Under-Wychwood – The Shaven Crown Hotel, High Street, Shipton-Under-Wychwood, Oxfordshire OX7 6BA. Tel: 01993 830330

Shrewsbury – Upper Brompton Farm, Cross houses, Shrewsbury, Shropshire SY5 6LE. Tel: 01743 761629

Simonsbath (Exmoor) – Simonsbath House Hotel, Simonsbath, Exmoor, Somerset TA24 7SH. Tel: 01643 831259

Snape (Butley) – Butley Priory, Nr Woodbridge, Suffolk IP12 3NR. Tel: 01394 450046

St Ives (Trink) – The Countryman At Trink Hotel, Old Coach Road, St Ives, Cornwall TR26 3JQ. Tel: 01736 797571

St Mawes (Ruan Highlanes) – The Hundred House Hotel, Ruan Highlanes, Truro, Cornwall TR2 5JR. Tel: 01872 501336

Stanhope (Weardale) – Horsley Hall, Eastgate, Nr Stanhope, Bishop Auckland, Co.Durham DL13 2LJ. Tel: 01388 517239

Stanwell (Nr Heathrow) – Stanwell Hall, Town Lane, Stanwell, Nr Staines, Middlesex TW19 7PW. Tel: 01784 252292

Staverton (Nr Totnes) – Kingston House, Staverton, Totnes, Devon TQ9 6AR. Tel: 01803 762 235

Stevenage (Hitchin) – Redcoats Farmhouse Hotel & Restaurant, Redcoats Green, Nr Hitchin, Hertfordshire SG4 7JR. Tel: 01438 729500

Stonor (Henley-on-Thames) – The Stonor Arms Hotel, Stonor, Nr Henley-on-Thames, Oxfordshire RG9 6HE. Tel: 01491 638866

Stow-on-the-Wold – The Unicorn Hotel, Sheep Street, Stow-on-the-Wold, Gloucestershire GL54 1HQ. Tel: 01451 830257

Stow-On-The-Wold (Kingham) – The Tollgate Inn, Church Street, Kingham, Oxfordshire OX7 6YA . Tel: 01608 658389

Stratford-upon-Avon (Loxley) – Glebe Farm House, Loxley, Warwickshire CV35 9JW. Tel: 01789 842501

Sway – The Nurse's Cottage, Station Road, Sway, Lymington, Hampshire SO41 6BA. Tel: 01590 683402

Tarporley (Willington) – Willington Hall Hotel, Willington, Near Tarporley, Cheshire CW6 0NB. Tel: 01829 752321

Tewkesbury (Kemerton) – Upper Court, Kemerton, Tewkesbury, Gloucestershire GL20 7HY. Tel: 01386 725351

Thurlestone Sands (Nr Salcombe) – Heron House Hotel, Thurlestone Sands, Nr Salcombe, South Devon TQ7 3JY. Tel: 01548 561308

Tintagel (Trenale) – Trebrea Lodge, Trenale, Tintagel , Cornwall PL34 0HR. Tel: 01840 770410

Uckfield – Hooke Hall, High Street, Uckfield, East Sussex TN22 1EN. Tel: 01825 761578

Wadebridge (Washaway) – Trehellas House & Memories of Malaya Restaurant, Washaway, Bodmin, Cornwall PL30 3AD. Tel: 01208 72700

Wareham (East Stoke) – Kemps Country House Hotel & Restaurant, East Stoke, Wareham, Dorset BH20 6AL. Tel: 01929 462563

Warwick (Claverdon) – The Ardencote Manor Hotel & Country Club, Lye Green Road, Claverdon, Warwickshire CV35 8LS. Tel: 01926 843111

Wells – Beryl, Wells, Somerset BA5 3JP. Tel: 01749 678738

Wells – Glencot House, Glencot Lane, Wookey Hole, Nr Wells, Somerset BA5 1BH. Tel: 01749 677160

Wells (Coxley) – Coxley Vineyard, Coxley, Wells, Somerset BA5 1RQ. Tel: 01749 670285

Wem – Soulton Hall, Near Wem, Shropshire SY4 5RS. Tel: 01939 232786

Wimborne Minster – Beechleas, 17 Poole Road, Wimborne Minster, Dorset BH21 1QA. Tel: 01202 841684

Wincanton (Holbrook) – Holbrook House Hotel, Wincanton, Somerset BA9 8BS. Tel: 01963 32377

Windermere – Quarry Garth Country House Hotel, Windermere, Lake District, Cumbria LA23 1LF. Tel: 015394 88282

Windermere (Bowness) – Fayrer Garden House Hotel, Lyth Valley Road, Bowness-On - Windermere, Cumbria LA23 3JP. Tel: 015394 88195

Witherslack – The Old Vicarage Country House Hotel, Church Road, Witherslack, Grange-Over-Sands, Cumbria LA11 6RS. Tel: 015395 52381

Woodbridge – Wood Hall Country House Hotel, Shottisham, Woodbridge, Suffolk IP12 3EG. Tel: 01394 411283

York (Escrick) – The Parsonage Country House Hotel, Escrick, York, North Yorkshire YO19 6LF. Tel: 01904 728111

Yoxford – Hope House, High Street, Yoxford, Saxmundham, Suffolk IP17 3HP. Tel: 01728 668281

WALES

Aberdovey – Plas Penhelig Country House Hotel, Aberdovey, Gwynedd LL35 0NA. Tel: 01654 767676

Abergavenny (Glangrwyney) – Glangrwyney Court, Glangrwyney, Nr Crickhowell, Powys NP8 1ES. Tel: 01873 811288

Abergavenny (Govilon) – Llanwenarth House, Govilon, Abergavenny, Monmouthshire NP7 9SF. Tel: 01873 830289

Anglesey (Llangefni) – Tre-Ysgawen Hall, Capel Coch, Llangefni, Ynys Yuon LL77 7UR. Tel: 01248 750750

Betws-y-Coed – Tan-y-Foel, Capel Garmon, Nr Betws-y-Coed, Conwy LL26 0RE. Tel: 01690 710507

Brecon (Three Cocks) – Old Gwernyfed Country Manor, Felindre, Three Cocks, Brecon, Powys LD3 0SU. Tel: 01497 847376

Caernarfon – Ty'n Rhos Country Hotel, Seion Llanddeiniolen, Caernarfon, Gwynedd LL55 3AE. Tel: 01248 670489

Conwy – The Old Rectory, Llanrwst Road, Llansanffried Glan Conwy, Colwyn Bay, Conwy LL28 5LF. Tel: 01492 580611

Dolgellau (Ganllwyd) – Plas Dolmelynllyn, Ganllwyd, Dolgellau, Gwynedd LL40 2HP. Tel: 01341 440273

Fishguard (Welsh Hook) – Stone Hall, Welsh Hook, Haverfordwest, Pembrokeshire, Dyfed SA62 5NS. Tel: 01348 840212

Monmouth (Whitebrook) – The Crown At Whitebrook, Restaurant With Rooms, Whitebrook, Monmouth, Monmouthshire NP5 4TX. Tel: 01600 860254

Pwllheli – Plas Bodegroes, Nefyn Road, Pwllheli, Gwynedd LL53 5TH. Tel: 01758 612363

Swansea (Mumbles) – Norton House Hotel & Restaurant, Norton Road, Mumbles, Swansea, West Glamorgan SA3 5TQ. Tel: 01792 404891

Tenby (Waterwynch Bay) – Waterwynch House Hotel, Waterwynch Bay, Tenby, Pembrokeshire SA70 8JT. Tel: 01834 842464

Tintern – Parva Farmhouse and Restaurant, Tintern, Chepstow, Monmouthshire NP16 6SQ. Tel: 01291 689411

SCOTLAND

Ballater, Royal Deeside – Balgonie Country House, Braemar Place, Royal Deeside, Ballater, Aberdeenshire AB35 5NQ. Tel: 013397 55482

By Huntly (Bridge of Marnoch) – The Old Manse of Marnoch, Bridge of Marnoch, By Huntly, Aberdeenshire AB54 7RS. Tel: 01466 780873

Castle Douglas – Longacre Manor, Ernespie Road, Castle Douglas, Dumfries & Galloway DG7 1LE. Tel: 01556 503576

Comrie (Perthshire) – The Royal Hotel, Melville Square, Comrie, Perthshire PH6 2DN. Tel: 01764 679200

Dunfries (Thornhill) – Trigony House Hotel, Closeburn, Thornhill, Dunfriesshire DG3 5EZ. Tel: 01848 331211

Dunkeld – The Pend, 5 Brae Street, Dunkeld, Perthshire PH8 0BA. Tel: 01350 727586

Edinburgh (Dunfermline) – Garvock House Hotel, St. Johns Drive, Transy, Dunfermline, Fife KY12 7TU. Tel: 01383 621067

Fintry (Stirlingshire) – Culcreuch Castle Hotel & Country Park, Fintry, Loch Lomond, Stirling & Trossachs G63 0LW. Tel: 01360 860555

Glasgow – Nairns, 13 Woodside Crescent, Glasgow, G3 7UP. Tel: 0141 353 0707

Glen Cannich (By Beauly) – Mullardoch House Hotel, Glen Cannich, By Beauly, Inverness-shire IV4 7LX. Tel: 01456 415460

Helmsdale (Sutherland) – Navidale House Hotel, Helmsdale, Sutherland KW8 6JS. Tel: 01431 821 258

Inverness – Culduthel Lodge, 14 Culduthel Road, Inverness, Inverness-shire IV2 4AG. Tel: 01463 240089

Inverness – Maple Court & Chandlery Restaurant, No12 Ness Walk, Inverness, Inverness-shire IV3 5SQ. Tel: 01463 230330

Isle Of Harris – Ardvourlie Castle, Aird A Mhulaidh, Isle Of Harris, Western Isles HS3 3AB. Tel: 01859 502307

Isle Of Mull – Killiechronan, Killiechronan, Isle Of Mull, Argyllshire PA72 6JU. Tel: 01680 300403

Isle of Mull (Tobermory) – Highland Cottage, Breadalbane Street, Tobermory, Isle of Mull, Argyll PA75 6PD. Tel: 01688 302030

Isle of Skye (Portree) – Bosville Hotel & Chandlery Seafood Restaurant, Bosville Terrace, Portree, Isle of Skye IV51 9DG. Tel: 01478 612846

Kentallen Of Appin – Ardsheal House, Kentallen Of Appin, Argyll PA38 4BX. Tel: 01631 740227

Killiecrankie,By Pitlochry – The Killiecrankie Hotel, Killiecrankie, By Pitlochry, Perthshire PH16 5LG. Tel: 01796 473220

Kinlochbervie – The Kinlochbervie Hotel, Kinlochbervie, By Lairg, Sutherland IV27 4RP. Tel: 01971 521275

Leslie (Fife) – Balgeddie House Hotel, Balgeddie Way, Glenrothes, Fife KY6 3ET. Tel: 01592 742511

Loch Ness (Drumnadrochit) – Polmaily House Hotel, Drumnadrochit, Loch Ness, Inverness-shire IV3 6XT. Tel: 01456 450343

Lockerbie – The Dryfesdale Hotel, Lockerbie, Dumfriesshire DG11 2SF. Tel: 01576 202427

Maybole (Ayrshire) – Culzean Castle - The Eisenhower Apartment, Maybole, Ayrshire KA19 8LE. Tel: 01655 884455

Moffat – Well View Hotel, Ballplay Road, Moffat, Dumfriesshire DG10 9JU. Tel: 01683 220184

Nairn (Auldearn) – Boath House, Auldearn, Nairn, Inverness IV12 5TE. Tel: 01667 454896

Oban – Dungallan House Hotel, Gallanach Road, Oban, Argyllshire PA34 4PD. Tel: 01631 563799

Oban – The Manor House Hotel, Gallanch Road, Oban, Argyllshire PA34 4LS. Tel: 01631 562087

Pitlochry – Knockendarroch House, Higher Oakfield, Pitlochry, Perthshire PH16 5HT. Tel: 01796 473473

Port Of Menteith – The Lake Hotel, Port Of Menteith, Perthshire FK8 3RA. Tel: 01877 385258

Rothiemurchus (Highland) – Corrour House Hotel, Inverdruie, Aviemore, Inverness-shire PH22 1QH. Tel: 01479 810220

St. Andrews – The Argyle House Hotel, 127 Norton Street, St. Andrews, KY16 9AG. Tel: 01334 473387

St. Boswell By Melrose – Clint Lodge, St. Boswells, Melrose, Roxburgshire TD6 0DZ. Tel: 01835 822027

St Fillans (Perthshire) – The Four Seasons Hotel, St Fillans , Perthshire PH6 2NF. Tel: 01764 685333

Strathtummel (By Pitlochry) – Queen's View Hotel, Strathtummel, By Pitlochry, Perthshire PH16 5NR. Tel: 01796 473291

Tain (Ross-shire) – Glenmorangie House at Cadbol, Cadbol, Fearn, By Tain, IV20 1XP. Tel: 01862 871671

The Great Glen (Fort William) – Corriegour Lodge Hotel, Loch Lochy, By Spean Bridge, Inverness-shire PH34 4EB. Tel: 01397 712685

IRELAND

Caragh Lake Co Kerry – Caragh Lodge, Caragh Lake, Co Kerry. Tel: 00 353 66 9769115

Cashel Co Tipperary – Cashel Palace Hotel, Cashel, Co Tipperary. Tel: 00 353 62 62707

Connemara (Co Galway) – Ross Lake House Hotel, Rosscahill, Oughterard, Co Galway. Tel: 00 353 91 550109

Craughwell (Co.Galway) – St. Clerans, Craughwell, Co.Galway IRELAND. Tel: 00 353 91 846 555

Dublin – Aberdeen Lodge, 53-55 Park Avenue, Ailesbury Road, Dublin 4. Tel: 00 353 1 2838155

Dublin – Fitzwilliam Park, No5 Fitzwilliam Square, Dublin 2. Tel: 00 353 1 6628 280

Kilkee Co Clare – Halpins Hotel & Vittles Restaurant, Erin Street, Kilkee, Co Clare. Tel: 00 353 65 9056032

Killarney Co Kerry – Earls Court House, Woodlawn Junction, Muckross Road, Co Kerry. Tel: 00 353 64 34009

Kilmeaden (Co. Waterford) – The Old Rectory - Kilmeaden House, Kilmeaden, Co Waterford. Tel: 00 353 51 384254

Letterkenny (Co Donegal) – Castle Grove Country House Hotel, Ramelton Road, Letterkenny, Co Donegal. Tel: 00 353 745 1118

Riverstown,Co Sligo – Coopershill House, Riverstown, Co Sligo. Tel: 00 353 71 65108

Sligo,Co Sligo – Markree Castle, Colooney, Co Sligo. Tel: 00 353 71 67800

Wicklow,Co Wicklow – The Old Rectory, Wicklow Town, Co Wicklow. Tel: 00 353 404 67048

CHANNEL ISLANDS

Guernsey (Fermain Bay) – La Favorita Hotel, Fermain Bay, Guernsey GY4 6SD. Tel: 01481 35666

Guernsey (St Martin) – Bella Luce Hotel & Restaurant, La Fosse, St Martin, Guernsey, GY4 6EB. Tel: 01481 38764

Herm Island (Guernsey) – The White House, Herm Island, Guernsey, GY1 3HR. Tel: 01481 722159

Jersey (St Aubin) – Hotel La Tour, Rue de Croquet, St Aubin, Jersey, JE3 8BR. Tel: 01534 743770

Sark Island (Guernsey) – La Sablonnerie, Little Sark, Sark Island, Channel Isle GY9 0SD. Tel: 01481 832061

Johansens Recommended Hotels – Europe & The Mediterranean

ANDORRA

Andorra La Vella – Andorra Park Hotel, Les Canals 24, Andorra La Vella. Tel: +376 82 09 79

AUSTRIA

Alpbach – Romantik Hotel Böglerhof, Alpbach 166, 6236. Tel: +43 5336 5227

Altaussee – Landhaus Hubertushof, Puchen, 8992 Altaussee, Steiermark. Tel: +43 36 22 71 280

Bad Gastein – Hotel & Spa Haus Hirt, Kaiserhofstrasse 14, 5640 Bad Gastein. Tel: +43 64 34 27 97

Bad Hofgastein – Grand Park Hotel , Kurgartenstrasse 26, 5630 Bad Hofgastein. Tel: +43 6432 63560

Bad Hofgastein – Kur-Sport & Gourmethotel Moser, Kaiser-Franz-Platz 2, 5630 Bad Hofgastein. Tel: +43 6432 6209

Bad Kleinkirchheim – Almdorf "Seinerzeit", Fellacher Alm, 9564 Patergassen bei Bad Kleinkirchheim. Tel: +43 4275 7201

Baden bei Wien – Grand Hotel Sauerhof, Weilburgstrasse 11-13, 2500 Baden bei Wien. Tel: +43 2252 41251 0

Dürnstein – Hotel Schloss Dürnstein, 3601 Dürnstein. Tel: +43 2711 212

Graz – Schlossberg Hotel, Kaiser-Franz-Josef-Kai 30, 8010 Graz. Tel: +43 316 80700

Grünau Im Almtal – Romantik Hotel Almtalhof, 4645 Grünau Im Almtal. Tel: +43 7616 82040

Igls – Schlosshotel Igls, Viller Steig 2, 6080 Igls, Tirol. Tel: +43 512 37 72 17

Igls – Sporthotel Igls, Hilberstrasse 17, 6080 Igls, Tirol. Tel: +43 512 37 72 41

Kitzbühel – Romantik Hotel Tennerhof, Griesenauweg 26, 6370 Kitzbühel. Tel: +43 53566 3181

Klagenfurt – Hotel Palais Porcia, Neuer Platz 13, 9020 Klagenfurt. Tel: +43 463 51 1590

Lech – Sporthotel Kristiania, Omesberg 331 , 6764 Lech/Arlberg. Tel: +43 55 83 25 610

Oberlech – Hotel Goldener Berg, Lech, 6764. Tel: +43 5583 22050

Pörtschach Am Wörther See – Hotel Schloss Leonstein, Leonstein 1, Pörtschach Am Wörther See. Tel: +43 4272 28160

Salzburg – Hotel Auersperg, Auerspergstrasse 61, 5027 Salzburg. Tel: +43 662 88944

Salzburg – Hotel Schloss Mönchstein, Mönchsberg Park, City Center, 26-Joh, 5020 Salzburg. Tel: +43 662 84 85 55 0

Salzburg – Schloss Haunsperg, Oberalm bei Hallein, 5411 Salzburg. Tel: +43 62 45 80 662

Schwarzenberg im Bregenzerwald – Romantik-Hotel Gasthof Hirschen, Hof 14, 6867 Schwarzenberg. Tel: +43 55 12/29 44 0

Seefeld – Hotel Klosterbräu, 6100 Seefeld Tirol. Tel: +43 5212 26210

Seefeld – Hotel Viktoria, Geigenbühelweg 589 , 6100 Seefeld Tirol. Tel: +43 52 12 44 41

St Christoph – Arlberg Hospiz, St Christoph, 6580. Tel: +43 5446 2611

St Wolfgang am See – Romantik Hotel im Weissen Rössl, 5360 St Wolfgang am See, Salzkammergut. Tel: +43 61 38 23 060

Velden – Seeschlössl Velden, Klagenfurter Strasse 34, 9220 Velden. Tel: +43 4274 2824

Vienna – Ana Grand Hotel Wien, Kärntner Ring 9, 1010, Vienna. Tel: +43 1 515 80 0

Vienna – Hotel im Palais Schwarzenberg, Schwarzenbergplatz 9, 1030 Vienna. Tel: +43 1 798 4515

Zürs – Thurnhers Alpenhof, 6763 Zürs/Arlberg. Tel: +43 5583 2191

BELGIUM

Antwerp – Firean Hotel, Karel Oomsstraat 6, 2018 Antwerp. Tel: +32 3237 02 60

Bruges – Die Swaene, Steenhouwersdijk, 8000 Bruges. Tel: +32-50-34 27 98

Bruges – Hotel Acacia, Korte Zilverstraat 3A, 8000 Bruges. Tel: +32 50 34 44 11

Bruges – Hotel de Orangerie, Kartuizerinnenstraat10, 8000 Bruges. Tel: +32 50 34 16 49

Bruges – Hotel Hansa, N. Desparsstraat 11, 8000 Bruges. Tel: +32 50 33 84 44

Bruges – Hotel Jan Brito, Freren Fonteinstraat 1, 8000 Bruges. Tel: +32 50 33 06 01

Bruges – Hotel Montanus, Nieuwe Gentweg 78, 8000 Bruges. Tel: +32 50 33 11 76

Bruges – Hotel Prinsenhof, Ontvangersstraat 9, 8000 Bruges. Tel: +32-50- 34 26 90

Brussels – L'Amigo, 1-3 Rue de L'Amigo, 1000 Brussels. Tel: +32 2 547 47 47

Florenville – Hostellerie Le Prieuré De Conques, Rue Florenville 176, 6820 Florenville. Tel: +32 61 41 14 17

Lanaken – La Butte Aux Bois, Paalsteenlaan 90, 3620 Lanaken. Tel: +32 89 72 12 86

Malmedy – Hostellerie Trôs Marets, Route Des Trôs Marets , 4960 Malmédy. Tel: +32-80- 33 79 17

Marche-en-Famenne – Château d'Hassonville, 6900 Marche-en-Famenne. Tel: +32 84 31 10 25

Vieuxville – Chateau de Palogne, Route du Palogne 3, 4190 Vieuxville. Tel: +32 86 21 38 74

CYPRUS

Limassol – Le Meridien Limassol, PO Box 56560, 3308, Limassol. Tel: +357 5 634 000

Limassol – The Four Seasons Hotel, PO Box 57222, Limassol. Tel: +35 7 5 310 222

CZECH REPUBLIC

Prague – Hotel Hoffmeister, Pod Bruskou 7, Kralov, 11800 Prague 1. Tel: +420 2 510 17 111

Prague – Sieber Hotel & Apartments, Slezska 55, 130 00, Prague 3. Tel: +420 224 25 00 25

DENMARK

Faaborg – Steensgaard Herregårdspension, Steensgaard, 5600 Millinge, Faaborg. Tel: +45 62 61 94 90

Nyborg – Hotel Hesselet, Christianslundsvej 119, 5800 Nyborg. Tel: +45 65 31 30 29

GREAT BRITAIN

Aylesbury – Hartwell House, Oxford Road, Nr Aylesbury, Buckinghamshire, England HP17 8NL. Tel: +44 1296 747444

Bamburgh – Waren House, Waren Mill, Bamburgh, Northumberland, England NE70 7EE. Tel: +44 1668 214581

Bath – Lucknam Park, Colerne, Nr Bath, Wiltshire, England SN14 8AZ. Tel: +44 1225 742777

Berwick-Upon-Tweed – Tillmouth Park, Cornhill-on-Tweed, Nr Berwick-Upon-Tweed, Northumberland TD12 4UU. Tel: +44 1890 882255

Birmingham – The Burlington, 6 Burlington Arcade, 126 New STreet, Birmingham, West MIdlands, England B2 4JQ. Tel: +44 121 643 9191

Burrington – Northcote Manor, Burrington, Nr Umberleigh, Devon, England EX37 9LZ. Tel: +44 1769 560501

Clanfield – The Plough At Clanfield, Bourton Road, Clanfield, Oxfordshire OX18 2RB. Tel: +44 1367 810222

Jersey – The Atlantic Hotel, La Moye, St Brelade, Jersey JE3 8HE. Tel: +44 1534 44101

London, Chelsea – Draycott House Apartments, 10 Draycott Avenue, Chelsea, London SW3 3AA. Tel: +44 171 584 4659

London, Kensington – Pembridge Court Hotel, 34 Pembridge Gardens, London W2 4DX. Tel: +44 171 229 9977

London, Knightsbridge – Basil Street Hotel, Basil Street, London SW3 1AH. Tel: +44 171 581 3311

London, Knightsbridge – Beaufort House Apartments, 45 Beaufort Gardens, London SW3 1PN. Tel: +44 171 584 2600

London, Knightsbridge – The Beaufort, 33 Beaufort Gardens, Knightsbridge, London SW3 1PP. Tel: +44 171 584 5252

London, Knightsbridge – The Cliveden Town House, 26 Cadogan Gardens, London SW3 2RP. Tel: +44 171 730 6466

London, Mayfair – The Ascott Mayfair, 49 Hill Street, London W1X 7FQ. Tel: +44 171 499 6868

London – Number Eleven Cadogan Gardens, 11 Cadogan Gardens, Sloane Square, London SW3 2RJ. Tel: +44 171 730 7000

London – Swan Hellenic Minerva, 77 New Oxford Street, London WC1 1PP. Tel: +020 7800 2227

London – The Colonnade Town House, 2 Warrington Crescent, London, England W9 1ER. Tel: +44 20 7286 1052

London – The Dorchester, Park Lane, Mayfair, London WIA 2HJ. Tel: +44 171 629 8888

London – The Hempel, Hempel Garden Square, 31-35 Craven Hill Gardens, London W2 3EA. Tel: +44 171 298 9000

London – The Leonard, 15 Seymour Street, London W1H 5AA. Tel: +44 171 935 2010

London – The Lexham, 32–38 Lexham Gardens, Kensington, London, England W8 5JE. Tel: +44 20 7559 4444

London – The Milestone, 1-2 Kensington Court, London W8 5DL. Tel: +44 171 917 1000

London – Twenty Nevern Square, 20 Nevern Square, London, England WC1 1PP. Tel: +44 20 7565 9555

London South Kensington – Number Sixteen, 16 Sumner Place, London SW7 3EG. Tel: +44 171 589 5232

London, Wimbledon Common – Cannizaro House, West Side, Wimbledon Common, London SW19 4UE. Tel: +44 181 879 1464

Lynton – Hewitt's Hotel, North Walk, Lynton, Devon, England EX35 6HJ. Tel: +44 1598 752293

Stapleford – Stapleford Park, Nr Melton Mowbray, Leicestershire LE14 2EF. Tel: +44 1572 787522

Streatley-On-Thames, Reading – Swan Diplomat, Streatley-On-Thames, Reading, Berkshire RG8 9HR. Tel: +44 1491 873737

Windermere – Miller Howe, Rayrigg Road, Windermere, Cumbria LA23 1EY. Tel: +44 15394 42536

Windermere – Storrs Hall, Windermere, Cumbria, England LA23 3LG. Tel: +44 15394 47111

ESTONIA

Tallinn – Park Consul Schlössle, Pühavaimu 13-15, EE 10123 Tallinn. Tel: +372 699 7700

FINLAND

Hämeenlinna – Hotel Vanajanlinna, 13330 Harviala, Hämeenlinna. Tel: +358 3 619 65 65

FRANCE

Amboise – Chateau de Pray, Route De Charge, 37400, Amboise. Tel: +33 2 47 57 23 67

Avallon – Château de Vault de Lugny, 11 Rue de Château, 89200 Avallon. Tel: +33 3 86 34 07 86

Avallon – Hostellerie de la Poste, 13 place Vauban, 89200, Vauban. Tel: +33 3 86 34 16 16

Beaulieu-sur-Mer – La Réserve de Beaulieu, 5 Boulevard Général Leclerc, 06310 Beaulieu-sur-Mer. Tel: +33 4 93 01 00 01

Beaune – Ermitage de Corton, R.N. 74, 21200 Chorey-Les-Beaune. Tel: +33 3 80 22 05 28

Biarritz – Hôtel du Palais, Avenue de L'Impératrice, 64200 Biarritz. Tel: +33 5 59 41 64 00

Billiers – La Domaine de Rochevilaine, Pointe De Pen Lan, 56190 Billiers. Tel: +33 2 97 41 61 61

Boutigny Nr Barbizon – Domaine de Belesbat, Courdimanche-sur-Essonne, 91820, Bourtigny-sur-Essonne. Tel: +33 1 69 23 19 00

Castres – Château d'Aiguefonde, 81200 , Aiguefonde. Tel: +33 563 98 1370

Chambéry-le-Vieux – Château de Candie, Rue du Bois de Candie, 73000 Chambéry-le-Vieux. Tel: +33 47 99 66 300

Champigné – Château des Briottières, 49330 Champigné. Tel: +33 2 41 42 00 02

Chinon – Château de Danzay, RD 749, 37420 Chinon. Tel: +33 2 47 58 46 86

Colmar – Hôtel Les Têtes, 19 Rue De Têtes, 68000 Colmar. Tel: +33 3 89 24 43 43

Connelles – Le Moulin de Connelles, 39 Route d'Amfreville-Sous-Les-Monts, 27430 Connelles. Tel: +33 2 32 59 53 33

Corsica-Porticcio – Hotel Le Maquis, BP 94, 20166 Porticcio-Corsica. Tel: +33 4 95 25 05 55

Courchevel – Hôtel Annapurna, 73120 Courchevel, 1850. Tel: +33 4 79 08 04 60

Divonne-les-Bains – Le Domaine de Divonne, Avenue des Thermes, 01220 Divonne-Les-Bains. Tel: +33 4 50 40 3434

Épernay – Hostellerie La Briqueterie, 4 Route de Sézanne, Vinay, 51530 Epernay. Tel: +33 3 26 59 99 99

Eze Village – Château Eza, Rue De La Pise, 06360 Eze Village. Tel: +33 4 93 41 12 24

Gérardmer – Hostellerie Les Bas Rupts , , 88400 Gérardmer, Vosges. Tel: +33 3 29 63 09 25

Gressy-en-France/Chantilly – Le Manoir de Gressy, 77410 Gressy-en-France, Seine et Marne. Tel: +33 1 60 26 68 00

Grignan – Manoir de la Roseraie, Route de Valreas, 26230, Grignan. Tel: +33 4 75 46 58 15

Honfleur – La Chaumière, Route du Littoral, 14600 Honfleur. Tel: +33 2 31 81 63 20

Honfleur – La Ferme Saint Siméon, Rue Adolphe-Marais, 14600 Honfleur. Tel: +33 2 31 89 23 61

Honfleur – Le Manoir du Butin, Phare du Butin, 14600 Honfleur. Tel: +33 2 31 81 63 00

La Gouesniere/St Malo – Chateau de Bonaban, La Gouesniere, 35350. Tel: +33 299 58 24 50

Langeais – Château de Rochecotte, Saint Patrice, 37130 Langeais. Tel: +00 33 2 47 96 16 16

Les Issambres – Villa Saint Elme, Corniche des Issambres, 83380 Les Issambres. Tel: +33 4 94 49 52 52

Lyon – La Tour Rose, 22 Rue de Boeuf, 69005 Lyon. Tel: +33 4 78 37 25 90

Madieres-Ganges – Chateau de Madieres, Madieres-Ganges, 34170, Ganges. Tel: +33 4 67 73 84 03

Martillac – Les Sources de Caudalie, Chemin de Smith Haut-Lafitte, 33650, Martillac. Tel: +33 5 57 83 83 83

Megève – Hôtel Mont-Blanc, Place de l'Eglise, 74120 Megève. Tel: +33 4 50 21 20 02

Megève – Lodge Park Hôtel, 100 Route d'Arly, 74120 Megève. Tel: +33 4 50 93 05 03

Monestier – Château des Vigiers, 24240 Monestier. Tel: +33 5 53 61 50 00

Paris – Hôtel Buci Latin, 34 Rue de Buci, 75006 Paris. Tel: +33 1 43 29 07 20

Paris – Hôtel de Crillon, 10 Place de la Concorde, 75008 Paris. Tel: +33 1 44 71 15 00

Paris – Hôtel de L'Arcade, 9 Rue de L'Arcade, 75008 Paris. Tel: +33 1 53 30 60 00

Paris – Hotel Franklin D. Roosevelt, 18 rue Clement Marot, 75008, Paris. Tel: +33 1 53 57 49 50

Paris – Hôtel Le Parc, 55-57 avenue Raymond Poincare, 75116, Paris. Tel: +33 1 44 05 66 66

Paris – Hôtel le Saint-Grégoire, 43 Rue de l'Abbé Grégoire, 75006 Paris. Tel: +33 1 45 48 23 23

Paris – Hôtel Le Tourville, 16 Avenue de Tourville, 75007 Paris. Tel: +33 1 47 05 62 62

Paris – L'Hôtel, 13 rue des Beaux Arts, 75006 Paris. Tel: +33 1 43 25 27 22

Paris – L'Hôtel Pergolese, 3 Rue Pergolese, 75116 Paris. Tel: +33 1 53 64 04 04

Paris – La Villa Maillot, 143 Avenue de Malakoff, 75116, Paris. Tel: +33 1 53 64 52 52

Paris – Le Lavoisier, 21 rue Lavoisier, 75008, Paris. Tel: +33 1 53 30 06 06

Pleven – Le Manoir de Vaumadeuc, 22130 Pleven. Tel: +33 2 96 84 46 17

Rochefort-sur-Mer – Hotel De La Corderie Royale, Rue Audebert, BP 275 , 17300. Tel: +33 5 46 99 35 35

Roquebrune Cap-Martin/Monaco – Grand Hôtel Vista Palace , Route De La Grande Corniche, 06190 Roquebrune/Cap-Martin. Tel: +33 4 92 10 40 00

Saint Tropez – Hôtel Sube, 15 Quai Suffren, 83990 St Tropez. Tel: +33 4 94 97 30 04

What does your paper say about you?

Jeremy Hoskins, hotelier, chooses Conqueror* Contour in Oyster, printed in colour.

Starring role. Jeremy Hoskins combed the Conqueror* range to discover the perfect texture for his hotel's letterhead. Ideal for brochures, menus, wine-lists and letterheads, as well as for all corporate and conference stationery, the colours, textures and weights of the Conqueror* range are the best in the business. For a free sample pack or advice on the Conqueror* range and where to find it, call + 44 (0) 1256 728665 or visit www.conqueror.com now. You'll get five stars for presentation.

⭐ Star quality. For a free sample pack or advice on the Conqueror* range and where to find it, call + 44 (0) 1256 728665 or visit www.conqueror.com now.

Saint Tropez – La Résidence de la Pinède, Plage de la Bouillabaisse, 83991 Saint Tropez. Tel: +33 4 94 55 91 00

Saint-Rémy-de-Provence – Château des Alpilles, Route Départementale 31, Ancienne route du Grés, 13210 St-Rémy-de-Provence. Tel: +33 4 90 92 03 33

Sainte- Maxime/Bay Of St Tropez – Hotel Le Beauvallon, Baie de St. Tropez, Beauvallon-Grimaud, 83120 Sainte-Maxime. Tel: +33 4 94 55 78 88

Sarlat-Vitrac – Domaine de Rochebois, Route du Château de Montfort, 24200 Vitrac. Tel: +33 5 53 31 52 52

Sciez sur Leman – Château de Coudrée, Domaine de Coudrée, Bonnatrait, 74140 Sciez sur Leman. Tel: +33 4 50 72 62 33

Serre-Chevalier – L'Auberge du Choucas, 05220, Monetier-Les-Bains, 1550 Serre-Chevalier . Tel: +33 4 92 24 42 73

Vervins – La Tour Du Roy, 45 rue du Général Leclerc, 02140, Vervins. Tel: +33 3 23 98 00 11

GERMANY

Badenweiler – Hotel Römerbad, Schlossplatz 1, 79410, Badenweiler. Tel: +49 76 32 70 0

Göttingen – Burghotel Hardenberg, 37176 Nörten-Hardenberg. Tel: +49 5503 9810

Munich – Hotel Königshof, Karlsplatz 25, 80335 Munich. Tel: +49 89 551 360

Niederstotzingen – Schlosshotel Oberstotzingen, Stettener Strasse 35-37 , 89168 Niederstotzingen. Tel: +49 7325 1030

Oberwesel/Rhein – Burghotel Auf Schönburg, 55430 Oberwesel/Rhein. Tel: +49 67 44 93 93 0

Rothenburg ob der Tauber – Hôtel Eisenhut, Herrngasse 3-7, 91541. Tel: +49 9861 70 50

Triberg – Romantik Parkhotel Wehrle, Gartenstr.24, 78098, Triberg. Tel: +49 7722 86020

Waldeck – Hotel Schloss Waldeck, , 34513 Waldeck. Tel: +49 5623 5890

Wassenberg – Hotel Burg Wassenberg, Kirchstrasse 17, 41849 Wassenberg. Tel: +49 2432 9490

Wernberg-Köblitz – Hotel Burg Wernberg, Schlossberg 10, 92533 Wernberg-Köblitz, Wernberg-Köblitz. Tel: +49 9604 9390

GIBRALTAR

Gibraltar – The Rock Hotel, 3 Europa Road. Tel: +350 73 000

GREECE

Athens – Hotel Pentelikon, 66 Diligianni Street, 14562 Athens. Tel: +30 1 62 30 650 6

Crete – St Nicolas Bay Hotel, Agios Nicholaos, Crete, 72100. Tel: +30 841 25 041

Evritania-Karpenissi – Hotel Club Montana, , Karpenissi 36100. Tel: +30 237 80400

Samos Island – Doryssa Bay Hotel-Village, Pythagorion, Samos Island, Aegean Island, 83103. Tel: +30 273 613 60

Santorini Island – Esperas Traditional Houses, Oia Santorini, 84702. Tel: +30 286 71088

HUNGARY

Budapest – Danubius Hotel Gellért, St.Gellért Tér 1, 1111 Budapest. Tel: +36 1 185 2200

Lake Balaton – Hotel Erika, Bathyany u.6, 8237, Tihany. Tel: +36 87 44 86 44

ISRAEL

Jerusalem – The American Colony, PO Box 19215, Jerusalem. Tel: +972 2 6279 777

ITALY

Assisi – Romantik Hotel Le Silve di Armenzano, Loc. Armenzano, 06081 Assisi. Tel: +39 075 801 90 00

Breuil-Cervinia – Hotel Bucaneve, Piazza Jumeaux 10, 11021 Breuil-Cervinia. Tel: +39 0166 949119/948386

Castellina In Chianti – Romantik Hotel Tenuta Di Ricavo, Localita Ricavo 4, 53011 Castellina In Chianti. Tel: +39 0577 740221

Castello Di Montegridolfo – Palazzo Vivani Castello Di Montegridolfo, Via Roma 38, Montegridolfo 47837. Tel: +39 0541 855350

Como – Albergo Terminus, Lungo Lario Trieste 14, 22100 Como. Tel: +39 031 329111

Como – Hotel Villa Flori, Via Cernobbio 12, 22100 Como. Tel: +39 031 573105

Etna – Hotel Villa Paradiso Dell' Etna, Via per Viagrande 37, 95037 SG La Punta. Tel: +39 751 2409

Ferrara – Albergo Annunziata, Piazza Repubblica 5, 44100 Ferrara. Tel: +39 0532 20 11 11

Ferrara – Ripagrande Hotel, Via Ripagrande 21, 44100 Ferrara. Tel: +39 0532 765250

Florence – Hotel J &J, Via Mezzo 20, 50121 Florence. Tel: +39 55 26312

Ischia – Hotel Miramare E Castello, Via Pontano 9, 80070 Ischia (NA). Tel: +39 081 991333

Italian Riviera – Hotel Punta Est, Via Aurelia 1, Finale Ligure, 17024. Tel: +39 019 600 611

Lido – Albergo Quattro Fontane, 30126, Lido di Venezia. Tel: +39 041 5260227

Lucca – Locanda l'Elisa, Via Nuova per Pisa, 1952, 55050 Massa Pisana, Lucca. Tel: +39 0583 379737

Madonna Di Campiglio – Hotel Lorenzetti, Via Dolomiti Di Campiglio 119, 38084 Madonna Di Campiglio (TN). Tel: +39 0 465 44 1404

Mantova – Albergo San Lorenzo, Piazza Concordia 14, 46100 Mantova. Tel: +39 0376 220500

Marling-Méran – Romantic Hotel Oberwirt, St Felixweg 2, 39020 Marling/Méran. Tel: +39 0473 44 71 11

Mauls – Romantik Hotel Stafler, Mauls 10, 39040 Freienfeld. Tel: +39 0472 771136

Milan – Hotel Auriga, Via Pirella 7, 20124 Milan. Tel: +39 02 66 98 58 51

Novi Ligure – Relais Villa Pomela, Via Serravalle 69, 15067 Novi Ligure (AL). Tel: +39 0143 329910

Pievescola – Hotel Relais La Suvera, 53030 Pievescola, Siena. Tel: +39 0577 960 300

Porto Ercole – Il Pellicano, , Aeralita Cala Dei Santi, 58018 Porto Ercole (GR). Tel: +39 0564 858111

Portobuffolé-Treviso – Romantik Hotel Villa Giustinian, Via Giustiniani 11, 31019 Portobuffolé-Treviso. Tel: +39 0422 850244

Positano – Romantik Hotel Poseidon, Via Pasitea 148, 84017 Positano. Tel: +39 089 81 11 11

Rimini – Il Grand Hotel Di Rimini, Parco Federico Fellini, 47900 Rimini. Tel: +39 0541 56000

Rome – Hotel Farnese, Via Alessandro Farnese 30 , (Anglo Viale Giulio Cesare), 00192 Rome. Tel: +39 06 321 25 53

Rome – Hotel Giulio Cesare, Via Degli Scipioni 287, 00192 Rome. Tel: +39 06 321 0751

Rome – Romantik Hotel Barocco, Piazza Barberini 9, 00187 Rome. Tel: +39 0 6 4872001

Rome-Palo Laziale – La Posta Vecchia, Palo Laziale, 00055 Ladispoli, Rome. Tel: +39 06 9949 501

Salerno-Santa Maria di Castellabate – Hotel Villa Sirio, Via Lungomare De Simone 15, 84072 Santa Maria di Castellabate. Tel: +39 0974 960 162

Saturnia – Hotel Terme Di Saturnia , 58050 Saturnia, Grosseto. Tel: +39 0 564 601061

Sestri Levante – Grand Hotel Villa Balbi, Viale Rimembranza 1, 16039 Sestri Levante. Tel: +39 0185 42941

Sorrento – Grand Hotel Cocumella, Via Cocumella 7, 80065 Sant'Agnello, Sorrento. Tel: +39 081 878 2933

Sorrento – Grand Hotel Excelsior Vittoria, Piazza Tasso 24, Sorrento-(Napoli). Tel: +39 081 80 71 044

South Tyrol Nova Levante – Posthotel Weisses Rössl, Via Carezza 30, 39036 Nova Levante (BZ), Dolomites. Tel: +39 0 471 613113

Südtirol-Völs am Schlern – Romantik Hotel Turm, Piazza Della Chiesa 9, Fié Allo Scilari, Bolzano. Tel: +39 0471 725014

Taormina Mare – Hotel Villa Sant' Andrea, Via Nazionale 137, 98030 Taormina Mare. Tel: +39 0942 23125

Taormina – Hotel Villa Diodoro, Via Bagnoli Croci 75, 98039 Taormina (ME). Tel: +39 0942 23312

Taormina-Sicily – Grande Albergo Capotaormina, Via Nazionale 105, 98039 Taormina. Tel: +39 0942 576015

Torino – Hotel Victoria, Via N.Costa 4, 10123 Torino. Tel: +39 011 56 11 909

Tuscan Riviera – Hotel Villa Undulna, Viale Marina, 54030 Cinquale Di Montignoso. Tel: +39 0585 807788

Varese Lake - Malpensa – Romantik Hotel Locanda Dei Mai Intees, Via Nobile Claudio Riva 2, 21022 Azzate (VA). Tel: +39 0332 457223

Venice – Hotel Metropole, San Marco- Riva Degli Schiavoni 4149, 30122 Venice. Tel: +39 041 52 05 044

Venice – Villa Condulmer, 31020 Zerman Di Mogliani Veneto, Treviso. Tel: +39 041 45 71 00

Vicenza-Arcugnano – Hotel Villa Michelangelo, Via Sacco 19, 36057 Arcugnano (Vicenza). Tel: +39 0444 550300

LATVIA

Riga – Hotel de Rome, Kalkuiela 28, LV 1050 Riga. Tel: +37 1 708 7600

Riga – Hotel Konventa Seta, Kaleju Iela 9/11, LV 1050 Riga. Tel: +371 708 7501

LUXEMBOURG

Luxembourg City – Hotel Albert Premier, 2A rue Albert 1er, 1117. Tel: +352 442 4421

Remich – Hotel Saint Nicolas, 31 Esplanade, 5533 Remich. Tel: +352 69 8888

MONACO

Monte-Carlo – Hotel Hermitage, Square Beaumarchis BP277, MC 98005. Tel: +33 92 16 40 00

Monte Carlo – Monte Carlo Beach Hotel, Avenue Princess Grace, 06190 Roquebrune-Cap-Martin. Tel: +33 4 93 28 66 66

MOROCCO

Marrakech – Les Deux Tours, Douar Abiad- Circuit de la Palmeraie, Municipalite An-Natchil, Marrakech BP 513. Tel: +212 4 32 95 27

THE NETHERLANDS

Amsterdam – Ambassade Hotel, Herengracht 341, 1016 AZ Amsterdam. Tel: +31 20 5550222

Amsterdam – Seven One Seven, Prinsengracht 717, 1017 jw, Amsterdam. Tel: +31 20 42 70 717

Amsterdam – The Canal House Hotel, Keizersgracht 148, 1015 CX, Amsterdam. Tel: +31 20 622 5182

Beetsterzwaag – Bilderberg Landgoed Lauswolt, Van Harinxmawrg 10, Beetsterzwaag 9244 CJ. Tel: +31 512 38 12 45

Bergambacht – Hotel De Arendshoeve, Molenlaan 14, 2861 LB Bergambacht. Tel: +31 182 35 1000

Drunen – Hotel De Duinrand, Steergerf 2, 5151 RB Drunen. Tel: +31 416 372 498

Lattrop – Hotel De Holtwenjde, Spiekweg 7, 7635 LP, Lattrop. Tel: +31 541 229 234

Oisterwijk – Hotel Restaurant de Swaen, De Lind 47, 5061 HT Oisterwijk. Tel: +31 135 23 3233

Ootmarsum – Hotel de Wiemsel, Winhofflaan 2, 7631 HX Ootmarsum. Tel: +31 541 292 155

Voorburg – Restaurant-Hotel Savelberg, Oosteinde 14, 2271 EH Voorburg. Tel: +31 70 387 2081

NORWAY

Balestrand – Kvikne's Hotel, 6898 Balestrand. Tel: +47 57 69 11 01

Bergen – Grand Hotel Terminus, Zander Kaaesgt 6, PO Box 1100 Sentrum, 5001 Bergen. Tel: +47 55 31 16 55

Dalen – Dalen Hotel, PO Boks 123, 3880 Dalen. Tel: +47 35 07 70 00

Honefoss – Grand Hotel Honefoss, Stabellsgate 8, 3500 Honefoss. Tel: +47 32 12 27 22

Lofthus in Hardanger – Hotel Ullensvang, 5787 Lofthus in Hardanger. Tel: +47 53 66 11 00

Moss – Hotel Refsnes Gods, P.O Box 236, 1501, Moss. Tel: +47 69 27 83 00

Oslo – First Hotel Bastion, Postboks 27, Sentrum, Skippergaten 7, 0152 Oslo. Tel: +47 22 47 77 00

Sandane – Gloppen Hotel, 6860 Sandane. Tel: +47 57 86 53 33

Sandnes/Stavanger – Kronen Gaard Hotel, Vatne, 4300 Sandnes. Tel: +47 51 62 14 00

Solvorn – Walaker Hotell, 6879 Solvorn. Tel: +47 576 84 207

Voss) – Fleischers Hotel, 5700 Voss. Tel: +47 56 52 05 00

PORTUGAL

Armacao De Pera – Vilalara Thalasso, Praia das Gaivotas, 8365, Armacao De Pera. Tel: +351 82 320 000

Carvoeiro – Casa Domilu, Estrada De Benagil, Apartado 250, Praia Do Carvoeiro, 8400 Lagoa. Tel: +351 82 358 409

Faro – La Réserve, Santa Bárbara de Nexe, 8000 Faro, Algarve. Tel: +351 89 999474

Faro – Monte do Casal, Cerro do Lobo, Estoi , 8000 Faro, Algarve. Tel: +351 89 91503

Lagos – Romantik Hotel Vivenda Miranda, Porto de Mós, 8600 Lagos, Algarve. Tel: +351 82 763 222

Lisbon – Hotel Tivoli Lisboa, Av da Liberdade 185, 1250 Lisbon. Tel: +351 1 319 89 00

Madeira – Quinta Da Bela Vista, Caminho Do Avista Navios, 4, 9000 Funchal, Madeira. Tel: +351 91 764144

Pinhao – Vintage House Hotel, Lugar da Ponte, 5085 Pinhao. Tel: +351 54 730 230

Redondo – Convento de Sao Paulo, Aldeia Da Serra, 7170, Redondo. Tel: +351 66 98 91 60

Sintra – Hotel Palacio de Seteais, Rua Barbosa de Bocage, 10, Seteais, 2710 Sintra. Tel: +351 1 923 32 00

Sintra – Quinta de Sao Thiago, 2710 Sintra . Tel: +351 1 923 29 23

SPAIN

Almuñecar – Hotel Suites Albayzin Del Mar, Avenida Costa Del Sol, 23-18690 Almuñecar, (Granada). Tel: +34 958 63 21 61

Arcos De La Frontera – Hacienda El Santiscal, Avda. del Santiscal, 129 (Lago de Arcos), 11630 Arcos de la Frontera. Tel: +34 9 56 70 83 13

Barcelona – Hotel Claris, Pau Claris 150, 08009 Barcelona. Tel: +34 93 487 62 62

Barcelona – Hotel Colon, Avenida de la Catedral 7, 08002, Barcelona. Tel: +34 93 301 14 04

Barcelona – The Gallery, Rosselló 249, 08008, Barcelona. Tel: +34 93 415 99 11

Camprodon – Hotel Grevol, Crta. Camprodon A Setcases S/N, Llanars, 17869. Tel: +34 972 74 10 13

El Rocio Almonte – El Cortijo de los Mimbrales, Crta del Rocio A483, KM20, 21.750 Almonte (Huelva). Tel: +34 959 44 22 37

Ibiza – Pikes, San Antonio De Portmany, Isla De Ibiza, Balearic Islands. Tel: +34 971 34 22 22

Lloret de Mar – Hotel Rigat Park, Playa de Fenals, 17310 Lloret de Mar, Costa Brava. Tel: +34 972 36 52 00

Madrid – Villa Real, Plaza De Las Cortes 10, 28014 Madrid. Tel: +34 91420 37 67

Malaga – La Posada Del Torcal, 29230 Villanueva de la Concepción, Malaga. Tel: +34 9 5 203 11 77

Mallorca – Gran Hotel Son Net, Castillo Son Net, 07194 Puigpunyent, Mallorca. Tel: +34 971 147 000

Mallorca – Hotel Monnaber Nou, Possessio de Monnaber Nou, 07310, Campanet, Mallorca. Tel: +34 971 877 176

Mallorca – Hotel Vistamar De Valldemosa, Ctra. Valldemosa, Andratx Km 2, 07170 Valldemosa , Mallorca. Tel: +34 971 61 23 00

Mallorca – Read's, Ca'n Moragues, 07320 Santa Marta, Mallorca. Tel: +34 9 971 140 262

Marbella – Hotel Los Monteros, 29600, Marbella. Tel: +34 952 82 38 46

Marbella – Hotel Puente Romano, P.O Box 204, 29600 Marbella. Tel: +34 9 52 82 09 00

Marbella – Marbella Club Hotel, Boulevard Príncipe Alfonso von Hohenlohe s/n, 29600 Marbella. Tel: +34 95 282 22 11

Marbella/Estepona – Las Dunas Suites, Ctra de Cádiz Km163.5, 29689 Marbella-Estepona, (Malaga). Tel: +34 95 279 43 45

Mijas-Costa – Hotel Byblos Andalus, 29640 Mijas Golf, Apt.138., Fuengirola (Malaga). Tel: +34 95 246 0250

Oviedo – Hotel de la Reconquista, Gil de Jaz 16, 33004 Oviedo, Principado de Asturias. Tel: +34 98524 1100

Pals – Hotel La Costa, Avenida Arenales de Mar 3, 17526 Platja de Pals, Costa Brava. Tel: +34 972 66 77 40

Puerto de Santa Maria-Cádiz – Monasterio de San Miguel, Calte Larga 27, 11500 El Puerto de Santa Maria, Cádiz. Tel: +34 956 54 04 40

Salamanca – Hotel Rector, Rector Esperabe, 10-Apartado 399, 37008 Salamanca. Tel: +34 923 21 84 82

Seville – Cortijo Aguila Real, Crta.Guillena-Burguillos, KM4, 41210 Guillena, Seville. Tel: +34 95 578 50 06

Seville – Hacienda Benazuza, 41800 Sanlúcar la Mayor, Seville. Tel: +34 95 570 33 44

Sitges – Hotel Estela Barcelona, Avda. Port d'Aiguadolc s/n, 08870, Stiges (Barcelona). Tel: +34 938 11 45 45

Sotogrande/San Roque – The San Roque Club Suites Hotel, CN340, KM127, 5, 11360 Sotogrande/San Roque, (Cadiz). Tel: +34 956 613 030

Tarragona – Hotel Termes Montbrío Resort, Spa & Park, Carrer Nou, 38, 43340 Montbrío Del Camp, Tarragona. Tel: +34 9 77 81 40 00

Tenerife – Gran Hotel Bahia Del Duque, 38660 Adeje, Costa Adeje, Tenerife South. Tel: +34 922 74 69 00

Tenerife – Hotel Botánico, Avda. Richard J. Yeoward 1, Urb Botánico, 238400 Puerto de la Cruz, Tenerife. Tel: +34 922 38 14 00

Tenerife – Hotel Jardin Tropical, Calle Gran Bretana, 38670 Costa Adeje, Tenerife, Canary Islands. Tel: +34 922 746 000

Tenerife – Hotel San Roque, C/. Esteban de Ponte 32, 38450, Garachico, Tenerife. Tel: +34 922 13 34 35

Viladrau – Xalet La Coromina, Carretera De Vic S/N, 17406, Viladrau. Tel: +34 93 884 92 64

SWEDEN

Åre – Hotell Åregården, Box 6, 83013 Åre. Tel: +46 647 178 00

Borgholm – Halltorps Gästgiveri, 387 92 Borgholm. Tel: +46 485 85000

Gothenburg – Hotel Eggers, Drottningtorget, Box 323, 401 25 Gothenburg. Tel: +46 31 80 60 70

Lagan – Toftaholm Herrgård, Toftaholm P.A., 34014 Lagan. Tel: +46 370 44055

Söderköping – Romantik Hotel Söderköpings Brunn, Skönbergagatan 35, Box 44, 614 21 Söderköping. Tel: +46 121 109 00

Stockholm – Hotell Diplomat, Strandvägen 7C, Box 14059, 10440 Stockholm. Tel: +46 8 459 68 00

Tällberg – Romantik Hotel Åkerblads, 793 70 Tällberg. Tel: +46 247 50800

Tanndalen – Hotel Tanndalen, 84098 Tanndalen. Tel: +46 684 22020

SWITZERLAND

Burgdorf-Bern – Hotel Stadthaus, Kirchbühl 2, 3402, Burgdorf-Bern. Tel: +41 34 428 8000

Chateau d'Oex – Hostellerie Bon Accueil, 1837 Chateau d'Oex. Tel: +41 26 924 6320

Kandersteg – Royal Park ***** Hotel, 3718 Kandersteg. Tel: +41 33 675 88 88

Lucerne/ Luzern – Romantik Hotel Wilden Mann, Bahnhofstrasse 30, 6000 Lucerne 7. Tel: +41 41 210 16 66

Lugano – Villa Principe Leopoldo & Residence, Via Montalbano, 6900 Lugano. Tel: +41 91 985 8855

Montreux – Villa Kruger, Villas Dubochet 17, 1815, Clarens. Tel: +41 21 98 92 110

Zermatt – Grand Hotel Zermatterhof, 3920, Zermatt. Tel: +41 27 966 66 00

Zuoz – Posthotel Engiadina, Via Maistra, Zouz. Tel: +41 81 85 41 021

TUNISIA

Tunis – La Maison Blanche, 45 Avenue Mohamed V, 1002, Tunis. Tel: +216 1 849 849

TURKEY

Istanbul – Hotel Sari Konak, Mimar Mehmet Aga Cad, No.42-46 34400 Sultanahmet, Istanbul. Tel: +90 212 638 62 58

Kalkan – Hotel Villa Mahal, P.K 4 Kalkan, 07960 Antalya. Tel: +90 242 844 3268

Kas – Club Savile, Cukurbag Yarimadasi, Kas, Antalya. Tel: +90 242 836 1393

Kas – Savile Residence, Cukurbag Yarimidasi, Kas, Antalya. Tel: +90 242 836 2300

Johansens Recommended Hotels – Southern Africa, Mauritius, The Seychelles

BOTSWANA

Kalahari – Jack's Camp, PO Box 173, Francistown. Tel: +27 49 124 575

Okavango – Xugana Island Lodge, C/O Hartley's Safaris, Private Bag 48 Maun. Tel: +267 661806

Okavango Delta – Abu Camp- Elephant Back Safaris, Elephant Back Safaris, Private Bay 332. Tel: +267 661 260

MAURITIUS

Mauritius – Paradis, Mauritius House, 1 Portsmouth Road, GU2 5BL. Tel: +01483 533008

Mauritius – Royal Palm, Mauritius House, 1 Portsmouth Road, GU2 5BL. Tel: +01483 533008

NAMIBIA

Windhoek – Vingerklip Lodge, PO Box 443, Outjo. Tel: +264 61 220 324

SEYCHELLES

Victoria – Fregate Island Private, PO Box 330, Victoria. Tel: +248 324 545

SOUTH AFRICA

Eastern Cape (Graaff-Reinet) – Andries Stockenström Guest House & Restaurant, 100 Cradock Street. Tel: +27 49 892 4575

Eastern Cape (Grahamstown) – Auckland Country House, PO Box 997, Grahamstown 6140. Tel: +27 46 622 2401

Eastern Cape (Port Elizabeth) – Hacklewood Hill Country House, 152 Prospect Road, Walmer, Port Elizabeth. Tel: +27 41 58 11 300

Eastern Cape (Port Elizabeth) – Shamwari Game Reserve, PO Box 32017, Summerstrand. Tel: +27 42 203 1111

Gauteng (Cullinan) – Zebra Country Lodge, PO Box 1090, Montana Park 0159. Tel: +27 12 735 1088/9

Gauteng (Magaliesburg) – De Hoek, PO Box 117, Magaliesburg. Tel: +27 014 577 1198

Gauteng (Pretoria) – Rovos Rail, P.O Box 2837, Pretoria 0001. Tel: +27 12 323 6052

Gauteng (Rozenhof) – Rozenhof Guest House, 525 Alexander Street, Brooklyn, Pretoria. Tel: +27 12 468 075

Kwazulu-Natal (Currys Post) – Old Halliwell Country Inn , PO Box 201, Howick 3290. Tel: +27 33 330 2602

Kwazulu-Natal (Durban) – Ridgeview Lodge, 17 Loudoun Road, Berea, Durban. Tel: +27 31 202 9777

Kwazulu-Natal (Lidgetton) – Happy Hill, Old Main Road, Lidgetton, 3270. Tel: +27 33 234 4380

Kwazulu-Natal (Lidgetton) – Lythwood Lodge, PO Box 17, Lidgetton 3270. Tel: +27 33 234 4666

Kwazulu-Natal (Maputaland) – Makakatana Bay Lodge, PO Box 65, Mtubatuba. Tel: +27 35 550 4189

Kwazulu-Natal (Maputaland) – Shayamoya Game Lodge, PO Box 784, Pongola 3170. Tel: +27 34 435 1110

Kwazulu-Natal (Mooi River Nr Giants Castle) – Hartford House, PO Box 31, Mooi River 3300. Tel: +27 33 263 2713

Kwazulu-Natal (Nottingham Road) – Hawklee Country House, PO Box 27, Nottingham Road 3280. Tel: +27 33 263 6209

Kwazulu-Natal (Pietermaritzburg) – Rehoboth Chalets, 276 Murray Road, Hayfields, Pietermaritzburg 3201. Tel: +27 331 962 312

Kwazulu-Natal (Rorke's Drift) – Fugitives Drift Lodge & Guest House, PO Rorkes Drift. Tel: +27 322 525 5789

Kwazulu-Natal (Shaka's Rock) – Comfort House, 27 Dolphin Crescent, Shaka's Rock. Tel: +27 322 525 5575

Kwazulu-Natal (Shakas Rock) – Lalaria Lodge, 25a Dolphin Crescent, Shakas Rock, Dolphin Coast. Tel: +27 322 525 5789

Kwazulu-Natal (Umhlali) – Isibindi Lodge, P.O. Box 275, Umhlali, 4390. Tel: +27 322 947 0538

Kwazulu-Natal (Umhlali) – Zimbali Lodge & Country Club, PO Box 404, Umhlali 4390. Tel: +27 117 80 7475

Kwazulu-Natal (Underberg) – Penwarn Country Lodge. Tel: +27 33 7011 777

Mozambique (Benguerra Island) – Benguerra Lodge, Box 87416, Houghton 2198. Tel: +27 11 483 27 34

Mpumalanga – Idube Game Reserve, PO Box 2617, Northcliff 2115. Tel: +27 11 888 3713

Mpumalanga (Hazyview) – Casa Do Sol, PO Box 57, Hazyview 1242. Tel: +27 13 737 8111

Mpumalanga (Kruger National Park) – Chitwa Chitwa Game Lodges, Head Office & Central Reservations, P.O Box 781854 Sandton , 2146. Tel: +27 11 883 1354

Mpumalanga (Malelale) – Buhala Country House, Kruger National Park, Box 165, Malelane 1320. Tel: +27 13 790 4372

Mpumalanga (Nelspruit) – Annandale House, 27 Rocket Street, Nelspruit. Tel: +27 82 7745 833

Mpumalanga (Nelspruit) – The Rest Country Lodge, PO Box 5900, Nelspruit. Tel: +27 13 744 9991/2

Mpumalanga (Timbavati) – Kings Camp, PO Box 427, Nelspruit 1200. Tel: +27 83 305 8130

Mpumalanga (White River) – Jatinga Country Lodge, Jatinga Road, White River, Mpumlanga. Tel: +27 13 751 5059

Mpumalanga (White River) – Leopard Hills Private Game Reserve, PO Box 612, Hazyview 1242. Tel: +27 13 737 6626/7

Mpumalanga (White River) – Savanna Tented Safari Lodge, PO Box 3619, White River 1240. Tel: +27 13 751 2205

Northern Cape (Kalahari) – Tswalu Private Desert Reserve, PO Box 420, Kathu. Tel: +27 53 781 9211

Northern Province (Hoedspruit) – Garonga Safari Camp, Makalali Conservancy, Hoedspruit 1380. Tel: +27 11 804 759

Northern Province (Hoedspruit) – Kapama Lodge, P.O Box 1511, Hoedspruit 1380. Tel: +27 12 804 4840

Northern Province (Hoedspruit) – Tshukudu Game Lodge, Main Road to Phalaborwa, Hoedspruit, Northern Province. Tel: +27 15 793 2476

Northern Province (Tzaneen) – Coach House, Tzaneen 0850. Tel: +27 15 307 3641

Northern Province (Waterberg) – Entabeni Game Reserve, PO Box 6349, Weltevreden Park. Tel: +27 11 675 0609

Northern Province (Welgevonden) – Makweti Safari Lodge, Welgevonden Game Reserve, P.O Box 310 , Vaalwater, 0530. Tel: +27 83 458 6122

Western Cape (Cape Town) – Cape Grace Hotel, West Quay, Victoria & Alfred Waterfront, Cape Town. Tel: +27 21 410 7100

Western Cape (Cape Town) – De Waterkant Lodge & Cottages, 20 Loader Street, De Waterkant, Cape Town 8001. Tel: +27 21 419 1097/77

Western Cape (Cape Town) – Villa Belmonte Manor House, 33 Belmont Avenue, Orangezicht, Cape Town. Tel: +27 21 462 1576

Western Cape (Cape Town-Higgovale) – Kensington Place, 38 Kensington Crescent, Higgovale, Cape Town. Tel: +27 21 424 4744

Western Cape (Cape Town-Seapoint) – The Clarendon, 67 Kloof Road, Fresnaye, Cape Town. Tel: +27 21 439 3224

Western Cape (Cape Town-Seapoint) – Huijs Haerlem, 25 Main Drive, Sea Point. Tel: +27 21 434 6434

Western Cape (Cape Town-Seapoint) – Winchester Mansions, 221 Beach Road, Sea Point. Tel: +27 21 434 2351

Western Cape (Cederberg Mountains) – Bushmans Kloof Wilderness Reserve, PO Box 53405 Kenilworth, Cape Town. Tel: +27 21 797 0990

Western Cape (Constantia Valley) – Steenberg Country Hotel, PO Box 10802, Steenberg Estate, Cape Town, 7945. Tel: +27 21 713 2222

Western Cape (Franschhoek) – La Couronne, Robertsvlei Road, Franschhoek 7690. Tel: +27 21 876 2770

Western Cape (Franschhoek) – Le Quartier Francais, 16 Huguenot Road, Franschhoek. Tel: +27 21 876 2151

Western Cape (Greyton) – Greyton Lodge, 46 Main Street, Greyton 7233. Tel: +27 28 254 9876

Western Cape (Hermon) – Bartholomeus Klip Farmhouse, PO Box 36, Hermon 7308. Tel: +27 22 448 1820

Western Cape (Hout Bay) – Tarragona Lodge, Cnr of Disa River Road & Valley Road, PO Box 26887, Hout Bay 7872. Tel: +27 21 790 5080

Western Cape (Knysna) – Belvidere Manor, Duthie Drive Belvedire Estate, Knynsa.

Western Cape (Little Karoo) – Mimosa Lodge, Church Street, Montague. Tel: +27 23 614 23 51

Western Cape (Mossel Bay) – Reins Coastal Nature Reserve, PO Box 298, Albertina. Tel: +27 28 735 3322

Western Cape (Newlands) – The Vineyard Hotel, Colinton Road, Newlands 7700, Cape Town. Tel: +27 21 683 3044

Western Cape (Northern Paarl) – Roggeland Country House, PO Box 7210, Northern Paarl, 7623. Tel: +27 21 868 2501

Western Cape (Oranjezicht) – No.1 Chesterfield, 1 Chesterfield Road, Oranjezicht, 8001 Cape Town. Tel: +27 21 461 7383

Western Cape (Plettenberg Bay) – Hog Hollow Country Lodge, PO Box 503, Plettenberg Bay, 6600. Tel: +27 4457 48879

Western Cape (Plettenberg Bay) – Laird's Lodge, PO Box 657, Plettenberg Bay, 6600. Tel: +27 4453 27721

Western Cape (Stellenbosch) – d'Ouwe Werf, 30 Church Street, Stellenbosch. Tel: +27 21 887 4608

Western Cape (Stellenbosch) – Lyngrove Country House, PO Box 7275, Stellenbosch 7599. Tel: +27 21 842 2116

Western Cape (Stellenbosch) – River Manor, No.6 The Avenue, Stellenbosch. Tel: +27 21 887 9944

Western Cape (Tulbagh) – Rijk's Ridge Country House, PO Box 340, Tulbagh. Tel: +27 23 230 1006

ZIMBABWE

Zimbabwe (Chiredzi-South East Lowveld) – Nduna Safari Lodge, Malilangwe Private Wildlife Reserve, Reservations P.O Box MP845 Mount Pleasant. Tel: +263 4 722 983

Zimbabwe (Chiredzi-South East Lowveld) – Pamushana, Malilangwe Private Wildlife Reserve, Reservations P.O Box MP845 Mount Pleasant. Tel: +263 4 722 983

Zimbabwe (Harare) – Meikles Hotel, Jason Moyo Avenue, PO Box 594, Harare. Tel: +263 4 707721

Zimbabwe (Harare) – Wild Geese Lodge, Buckland Lane, Teviotdale, Harare. Tel: +263 4 860466/275

Zimbabwe (Hwange) – The Hide Safari Camp, 27-29 James Martin Drive, PO Box ST274, Southerton. Tel: +263 4 660554

Zimbabwe (Lake Cariba) – Sanyati Lodge, 124 Josiah Chinamano, Harare. Tel: +263 4 72 22 33

Zimbabwe (Nyanga) – Inn on Rupurara, PO Box 337, Juliasdale. Tel: +263 20 67449

Zimbabwe (Victoria Falls) – Victoria Falls Hotel, Mallet Drive, Victoria Falls. Tel: +263 13 4761

Johansens Recommended Hotels – North America, Bermuda & The Caribbean

BERMUDA

Hamilton – Rosedon Hotel, Pitts Bay Road, PO Box HM 290, Hamilton HMCX. Tel: +1 441 295 1640

Paget – The Newstead Hotel, 27 Harbour Road, Paget PG02. Tel: +1 1 441 236 6060

Paget – Harmony Club All Inclusive, PO Box 299, South Shore Road, Paget PG BX. Tel: +1 441 236 3500

Paget – Fourways Inn, PO Box PG 294, Paget PG BX. Tel: +1 441 236 6517

Warwick – Surf Side Beach Club, 90 South Shore Road, PO Box WK 101, Warwick. Tel: +1 441 236 7100

CARIBBEAN

Antigua – The Inn At English Harbour, PO Box 187, St Johns, Antigua. Tel: +1 268 460 1014

Curacao – Avila Beach Hotel, Penstraat 130, Willemstad, Curacao. Tel: +599 9 461 4377

Dominica – Hummingbird Inn, Morne Daniel, Box 1901, Roseau, Dominica. Tel: +1 767 449 1042

Martinique – Manoir De Beauregard, Chemin Des Salines 97227, Sainte Anne, Frenc. Tel: +596 76 73 40

St Lucia – Mago Estate Hotel, PO Box 434. Tel: +1 758 459 5880

St Vincent – Grand View Beach Hotel, Villa Point, Box 173, St Vincent, West Indies. Tel: +1 809 458 4811

St Vincent & The Grenadines – Camelot Inn, PO Box 787, Kingstown, St Vincent & The Grenadines. Tel: +1 784 456 2100

Tobago – Coco Reef Resort, PO box 434, Scarborough, Tobago, West Indies. Tel: +1 868 639 8571

Turks & Caicos – Grace Bay Club, Grace Bay Road, PO Box 681, Providenciales, Provo Island. Tel: +1 649 946 5199

CANADA

Quebec, Ayer's Cliff – Auberge Ripplecove Inn, 700 Ripplecove Road, Ayer's Cliff, Quebec JOB 1C0. Tel: +1 819 838 4296

Sidney – Seaside Luxury Resort, 8355 Lockside Drive, Sidney, British Columbia. Tel: +1 250 544 1000

Vancouver – The West End Guest House, 1362 Haro Street, Vancouver, British Columbia V6 IG2. Tel: +1 604 681 2889/1302

Vancouver – The Wedgewood Hotel, 845 Hornby Street, Vancouver, British Columbia V6Z 1V1. Tel: +1 604 689 7777

Victoria – Dashwood Manor, 1 Cook Street, Victoria, British Columbia V8V 3W6. Tel: +1 250 385 5517

UNITED STATES OF AMERICA

Arizona (Flagstaff) – Inn at 410, 410 North Leroux Street, Flagstaff, Arizona 86001. Tel: +1 520 774 0088

Arizona (Phoenix) – Maricopa Manor, Box 7186, 15 West Pasadena Avenue, Phoenix, Arizona 85013-2001. Tel: +1 602 274 6302

Arizona (Sedona) – Canyon Villa Inn, 125 Canyon Circle Drive, Sedona, Arizona 86351. Tel: +1 520 284 1226

Arizona (Sedona) – Casa Sedona, 55 Hozoni Drive, Sedona, Arizona 86336. Tel: +1 520 282 2938

Arizona (Tucson) – Tanque Verde Ranch, 14301 East Speedway Boulevard, Tucson, Arizona 85748. Tel: +1 520 296 6275

Arizona (Tucson) – White Stallion Ranch, 9251 West Twin Peaks Road, Tucson, Arizona 85743. Tel: +1 520 297 0252

California (Carmel) – Pine Inn, PO Box 250, Ocean Avenue & Monte Verde, Carmel, California 93921. Tel: +1 408 624 3851

California (Elk) – Elk Cove Inn, 6300 South Highway One, PO Box 367, Elk, California 95432. Tel: +1 707 877 3321

California (Eureka) – Carter House, 301 L Street, Eureka, California 95501. Tel: +1 707 444 8062

California (Ferndale) – Gingerbread Mansion Inn, 400 Berding Street, (PO Box 40), Ferndale, California 95536-0040. Tel: +1 707 786 4000

California (Hollywood) – Le Parc Suite Hotel, 733 North West Knoll Drive, West Hollywood, California 90069. Tel: +1 310 855 8888

California (La Jolla) – The Bed & Breakfast Inn at La Jolla, 7753 Draper Avenue, La Jolla, California 92037. Tel: +1 619 456 2066

California (La Quinta) – Two Angels Inn, 78-120 Caleo Bay, La Quinta, California. Tel: +1 760 564 7332

California (Mendocino) – Joshua Grindle Inn, 44800 Little Lake Road, PO Box 647, Mendocino, California 95460. Tel: +1 707 937 4143

California (Monterey Peninsula) – The Martine Inn, 255 Oceanview Boulevard, Pacific Grove, California 93950. Tel: +1 831 373 3388

California (Muir Beach) – Pelican Inn, Highway 1, Muir Beach, California 94965. Tel: +1 415 383 6000

California (Napa Valley) – The Ink House, 1575 Helena Highway at Whitehall Lane, St Helena, California 94574-9775. Tel: +1 707 963 3890

California (Nevada City) – Red Castle Inn Historic Lodging, 109 Prospect Street, Nevada City, California 95959. Tel: +1 530 265 5135

California (Palm Springs) – The Willows, 412 West Tahquitz Canyon Way, Palm Springs, California 92262. Tel: +1 760 320 0771

California (San Francisco) – Nob Hill Lambourne, 725 Pine Street, San Francisco, California 94108. Tel: +1 415 433 2287

California (San Rafael) – Gerstle Park Inn, 34 Grove Street, San Rafael, California 94901. Tel: +1 415 721 7611

California (Santa Ana) – Woolley's Petite Suites, 2721 Hotel Terrace Road, Santa Ana, California 92705. Tel: +1 714 540 1111

California (Shasta) – Brigadoon Castle, 9036 Zogg Mine Road, PO Box 324, Igo, California 96047. Tel: +1 530 396 2785

California (Solvang) – The Alisal Guest Ranch & Resort, 1054 Alisal Road, Solvang, California 93463. Tel: +1 805 688 6411

California (Sutters Creek, Gold Country) – The Foxes Inn, 77 Main Street, Sutters Creek, California 95685. Tel: +1 209 267 5882

Colorado (Denver) – Historic Castle Marne, 1572 Race Street, Denver , Colorado 80206. Tel: +1 303 331 0621

Colorado (Durango) – Tall Timber, 1 Silverton Star, Durango, Colorado 81301. Tel: +1 970 259 4813

Connecticut (Deep River) – Riverwind Inn, 209 Main Street, Deep River, Connecticut 06417. Tel: +1 860 526 2014

Connecticut (Greenwich) – The Homestead Inn, 420 Fieldpoint Road, Greenwich, Connecticut 06830. Tel: +1 203 869 7500

Connecticut (New Preston) – The Boulders, East Shore Road, Route 45, PO Box 2575 New Preston, Connecticut 06777. Tel: +1 860 868 0541

Delaware (Montchanin) – The Inn at Montchanin Village, Route 100 & Kirk Road, Montchanin, Delaware 19710. Tel: +1 302 888 2133

Delaware (Rehoboth Beach) – Boardwalk Plaza Hotel, Olive Avenue & The Boardwalk, Rehoboth Beach, Delaware 19971. Tel: +1 302 227 0441

Florida (Duck Key) – Hawk's Cay Resort, 61 Hawk's Cay Blvd, , Duck Key, Florida 33050-3756. Tel: +1 305 743 7000

Florida (Fort Lauderdale) – Lago Mar, 1700 South Ocean Lane, Fort Lauderdale, Florida 33316. Tel: +1 954 523 6511

Florida (Holmes Beach) – Harrington House. Tel: +

Florida (Key West) – Island City House, 411 William Street, Key West, Florida 33040. Tel: +1 305 294 5702

Florida (Key West) – Simonton Court Historic Inn & Cottages, 320 Simonton Street, Key West, Florida 33040. Tel: +1 305 294 6386

Florida (Lake Wales) – Chalet Suzanne, 3800 Chalet Suzanne Drive, Lake Wales, Florida 33853-7060. Tel: +1 941 676 6011

Florida (Miami Beach) – The Richmond, 1757 Collins Avenue, Miami Beach, Florida 33139. Tel: +1 305 538 2331

Florida (Miami Beach) – Hotel Ocean, 1230-1238 Ocean Drive, South Beach, Florida 33139. Tel: +1 305 672 2579

Georgia (Cumberland Island) – Greyfield Inn , Cumberland Island, PO Box 900, Fernandina Beach, Florida 32035-0900. Tel: +1 904 261 6408

Georgia (Little St. Simons Island) – The Lodge on Little St. Simons Island, PO Box 21078, St Simons Island, Georgia. Tel: +1 912 638 7472

Georgia (Perry) – Henderson Village, 125 South Langston Circle, Perry, Georgia 31069. Tel: +1 912 988 8696

Georgia (Savannah) – Foley House Inn, 14 West Hull, Chippewa Square, Savannah, Georgia 31401. Tel: +1 912 232 6622

Georgia (Savannah) – The Eliza Thompson House, 5 West Jones Street, Savannah, Georgia 31401. Tel: +1 912 236 3620

Georgia (Savannah) – Presidents Quarters, 225 East President Street, Savannah, Georgia 31401. Tel: +1 912 233 1600

Georgia (Savannah) – Magnolia Place Inn, 503 Whittaker Street, Savannah, Georgia 31401. Tel: +1 912 236 7674

Georgia (Thomasville) – Melhana Plantation, 301 Showboat Lane, Thomasville, Georgia 31792. Tel: +1 912 266 2290

Hawaii (Kailua-Kona) – Kailua Plantation House, 75-5948 Alii Drive, Kailua-Kona, Hawaii 96740. Tel: +1 808 329 3727

Hawaii (Volcano Village, Big Island) – Chalet Kilauea-The Inn at Volcano, Box 998, Wright Road, Volcano Village, Hawaii 96785. Tel: +1 808 967 7786

Louisiana (Napoleonville) – Madewood Plantation House, 4250 Highway 308, Napoleonville, Louisiana 70390. Tel: +1 504 369 7151

Louisiana (New Orleans) – The Claiborne Mansion, 2111 Dauphine Street, New Orleans, Louisiana 70116. Tel: +1 504 949 7327

Louisiana (New Orleans) – Windsor Court, 300 Gravier Street, New Orleans, Louisiana 70130. Tel: +1 504 523 6000

Maine (Greenville) – The Lodge at Moosehead Lake, Upon Lily Bay Road, Box 1167, Greenville, Maine 04441. Tel: +1 207 695 4400

Maine (Kennebunkport) – Kennebunkport Inn, 1 Dock Square, PO Box 111, Kennebunkport, Maine 04046. Tel: +1 207 967 2621

Maine (Prouts Neck) – Black Point Inn Resort, Prouts Neck, Scarborough, Maine 04074. Tel: +1 207 883 4126

Maryland (Frederick) – Tyler Spite Inn, 112 West Church Street, Frederick, Maryland 21701. Tel: +1 301 831 4455

Maryland (Taneytown) – Antrim 1844, 30 Trevanion Road, Taneytown, Maryland 21787. Tel: +1 410 756 6182

Massachusetts (Boston Area) – A Cambridge House, 2218 Massachusetts Avenue, Cambridge, Massachusetts 02140-1836. Tel: +1 617 491 6300

Massachusetts (Cape Cod) – Wedgewood Inn, 83 Main Street, Route 6A, Yarmouth Port, Massachusetts 02675. Tel: +1 508 362 9178

Massachusetts (Chatham) – Pleasant Bay Village Resort, PO Box 772, Route 28, Chatham, Massachusetts 02633. Tel: +1 508 945 1133

Massachusetts (Chatham) – The Captain's House Inn, 369-377 Old Harbor Road, Chatham, Cape Cod, Massachusetts 02633. Tel: +1 508 945 0127

Massachusetts (Deerfield) – Deerfield Inn, 108 Old Main Street, Deerfield, Massachusetts 01342. Tel: +1 413 774 5587

Massachusetts (Eastham) – The Whalewalk Inn, 220 Bridge Road, Eastham, Massachusetts 02642. Tel: +1 508 255 0617

Massachusetts (Gloucester) – Ocean View Inn, 171 Atlantic Road, Gloucester, Massachusetts 01930. Tel: +1 978 283 6200

Massachusetts (Lenox) – Wheatleigh, Hawthorne Road, Lenox, Massachusetts 01240. Tel: +1 413 637 0610

Massachusetts (Rockport) – Seacrest Manor, 99 Marmion Way, Rockport, Massachusetts 01966. Tel: +1 978 546 2211

Mexico (Ixtapa/Zihuatanejo) – Hotel Villa Del Sol, Playa La Ropa s/n, PO Box 84. Tel: +1 52 755 4 2239

Michigan (Petoskey) – Staffords Perry Hotel, Bay at Lewis Street, Petoskey, Michigan 49770. Tel: +1 616 347 4000

Mississippi (Biloxi) – Father Ryan House, 1196 Beach Boulevard, Biloxi, Mississippi. Tel: +1 228 435 1189

Mississippi (Jackson) – Fairview Inn, 734 Fairview Street, Jackson, Mississippi 39202. Tel: +1 601 948 3429

Mississippi (Vicksburg) – The Duff Green Mansion, 1114 1st East Street, Vicksburg , Mississippi 39180. Tel: +1 601 636 6968

New Hampshire (Bedford) – Bedford Village Inn, 2 Village Inn Lane, Bedford, New Hampshire 03110. Tel: +1 603 472 2001

New Hampshire (Bethlehem) – Adair, 80 Guider Lane, Bethelehem, New Hampshire 03574. Tel: +1 603 444 2600

New Hampshire (Henniker) – Colby Hill Inn, The Oaks, PO Box 779, Henniker, New Hampshire 03242. Tel: +1 603 428 3281

New Hampshire (Jackson) – Inn at Thorn Hill, Thorn Hill Road, Jackson, New Hampshire 03846. Tel: +1 603 383 4242

New Jersey (Cape May) – The Queens Hotel, 601 Columbia Avenue, Cape May, New Jersey 08204. Tel: +1 609 884 1613

New Jersey (Hope) – The Inn at Millrace Pond, PO Box 359, Hope, New Jersey 07844. Tel: +1 908 459 4884

New York – The Iroquois, 49 West 44th Street, New York, New York 10036. Tel: +212 840 3080

New York (Cazenovia) – The Brewster Inn, 6 Ledyard Avenue, Cazenovia, New York 13035. Tel: +1 315 655 9232

New York (Clarence) – Asa Ransom House, 10529 Main Street, Route 5, Clarence, New York 14031-1684. Tel: +1 716 759 2315

New York (East Aurora) – The Roycroft Inn, 40 South Grove Street, East Aurora, New York 14052. Tel: +1 716 652 5552

New York (Ithaca) – Benn Conger Inn, 206 West Cortland Street, Groton, New York 13073. Tel: +1 607 898 5817

North Carolina (Lake Toxaway) – The Greystone Inn, , Lake Toxaway, North Carolina 28747. Tel: +1 828 966 4700

North Carolina (Pittsboro) – The Fearrington House, 2000 Fearrington Village Center, Pittsboro, North Carolina 27312. Tel: +1 919 542 2121

North Carolina (Saluda) – Orchard Inn, Highway 176, Box 725, Saluda, North Carolina 28773. Tel: +1 828 749 5471

North Carolina (Tryon) – Pine Crest, 200 Pine Crest Lane, Tryon, North Carolina 28782. Tel: +1 828 859 9135

North Carolina (Waynesville) – The Swag Country Inn, 2300 Swag Road, Waynesville, North Carolina 28786. Tel: +1 828 926 0430

Oregon (Ashland) – The Winchester Country Inn, 35 South Second Street, Ashland, Oregon 97520. Tel: +1 541 488 1113

Oregon (Eugene) – Campbell House, 252 Pearl Street, Eugene, Oregon 97401. Tel: +1 541 343 1119

Oregon (Hood River) – Columbia Gorge Hotel, 4000 Westcliff Drive, Hood River, Oregon 97031-9970. Tel: +1 541 386 5566

Pennsylvania (South Sterling) – The French Manor, Huckleberry Road (Route 191), BOX 39, South Sterling, Pennsylvania 18460. Tel: +1 717 676 3244

Rhode Island (Newport) – Cliffside Inn, 2 Seaview Avenue, Newport, Rhode Island 02840. Tel: +1 401 847 1811

South Carolina (Beaufort) – The Rhett House Inn, 1009 Craven Street, Beaufort, South Carolina 29902. Tel: +1 843 524 9030

South Carolina (Charleston) – Wentworth Mansion, 149 Wentworth Street, Charleston, South Carolina 29401. Tel: +1 843 853 1886

South Carolina (Pawleys Island) – Litchfield Plantation, Kings River Road, Pawleys Island, South Carolina 29585. Tel: +1 843 237 9121

Utah (Salt Lake City) – The Inn On Capitol Hill, 225 North State Street, Salt Lake City, Utah 84103. Tel: +1 801 575 1112

Utah (Salt Lake City) – La Europa Royale, 1135 East Vine Street, Salt Lake City, Utah 84121. Tel: +1 801 263 7999

Vermont (Chittenden) – Mountain Top Inn & Resort, Mountain Top Road, Chittenden, Vermont 05737. Tel: +1 802 483 2311

Vermont (Chittenden) – Tulip Tree Inn, Chittenden Dan Road, Chittenden, Vermont 05737. Tel: +1 802 483 6213

Vermont (Lower Waterford) – Rabbit Hill Inn, 48 Lower Waterford Road, Lower Waterford, Vermont 05848. Tel: +1 802 748 5168

Vermont (Manchester Village) – 1811 House, PO Box 39, Route 7A, Manchester Village, Vermont 05254. Tel: +1 802 362 1811

Vermont (Stowe) – The Mountain Road Resort, PO Box 8, 1007 Mountain Road, Stowe, Vermont 05672. Tel: +1 802 253 4566

Vermont (Vergennes) – Basin Harbor Club, On Lake Champlain, Vergennes, Vermont 05491. Tel: +1 802 475 2311

Vermont (West Townshend) – Windham Hill Inn, , West Townshend, Vermont 05359. Tel: +1 802 874 4080

Virginia (Charlottesville) – Clifton-The Country Inn & Estate, 1296 Clifton Inn Drive, Charlottesville, Virginia 22941. Tel: +1 804 971 1800

Washington (Orcas Island) – Turtleback Farm Inn, 1981 Crow Valley Road, Eastsound, Washington 98245. Tel: +1 360 376 4914

Washington (Port Townsend) – Ann Starrett Mansion, 744 Clay Street, Port Townsend, Washington 98368. Tel: +1 360 385 3205

Washington (Seattle) – Sorrento Hotel, 900 Madison Street, Seattle, Washington 98104-9742. Tel: +1 206 622 6400

Wisconsin (Sturgeon Bay) – Inn at Cedar Crossing, 336 Louisiana Street, Sturgeon Bay, Wisconsin 54235. Tel: +1 920 743 4200

Wyoming (Cheyenne) – Nagle Warren Mansion 1888, 222 E.17th Street, Cheyenne, Wyoming 82001. Tel: +1 307 637 3333

Wyoming (Jackson Hole) – The Alpenhof Lodge, Teton Village, Jackson Hole, Wyoming 83025. Tel: +1 307 733 3242

Hildon Ltd., Broughton, Hampshire SO20 8DG, ☎ 01794 - 301 747

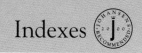

Indexes

85

Recommended Cottages, Houses & Apartments with fishing on site

Recommended Cottages, Houses & Apartments with golf on site

Recommended Cottages, Houses & Apartments with tennis on site

Recommended Cottages, Houses & Apartments with outdoor pool

Recommended Cottages, Houses & Apartments with indoor pool

ENGLAND

SCOTLAND

Recommended Cottages, Houses & Apartments with disabled facilities

ENGLAND

SCOTLAND

Recommended Cottages, Houses & Apartments with prepared meals available

ENGLAND

SCOTLAND

Recommended Cottages, Houses & Apartments accepting dogs

ENGLAND

SCOTLAND

Johansens Preferred Partners

ORDER FORM

Call our 24hr credit card hotline FREEPHONE 0800 269 397.

Simply indicate which title(s) you require by putting the quantity in the boxes provided. Choose your preferred method of payment and mail to Johansens, FREEPOST (CB 264), 43 Millharbour, London E14 9BR, England (no stamp needed). Your FREE gifts will automatically be dispatched with your order. Fax orders welcome on 0171 537 3594

CHOOSE FROM 7 SPECIAL GUIDE COLLECTIONS – SAVE UP TO £56

TITLE	Normal Price	PRICE	SAVE	QTY	TOTAL
OFFER ONE – The Basic Collection					
3 Johansens Guides A+B+C	£42.85	£36.00	£6.85		
OFFER TWO – The Extended Collection					
4 Johansens Guides A+B+C+G	£58.80	£46.00	£12.80		
OFFER THREE – The Full Selection					
5 Johansens Guides A+B+C+G+K PLUS Southern Africa Guide **FREE**	£71.75	£56.00	£15.75		
OFFER FOUR - The Executive Collection					
Business Meeting Venues Guide & CD-ROM M+R	£40.00	£30.00	£10.00		
OFFER FIVE - The Holiday Pack					
3 Johansens Guides D+E+F	£18.93	£9.99	£8.94		
OFFER SIX - The Digital Collection					
3 Johansens CD-ROMs N+O+P PLUS Southern Africa CD-ROM Q **FREE**	£69.85	£59.85	£10.00		
OFFER SEVEN - The Chairman's Collection					
Business Meeting Venues Guide & CD-ROMs M+R PLUS 5 Johansens Boxed Guides A+B+C+G+K, PLUS D+E+F, PLUS 3 CD-ROMs N+O+P PLUS Southern Africa Guide/CD ROM Q **FREE**, PLUS Mystery Gift **FREE**	£205.53	£149.00	£56.53		
Privilege Card	£20.00	**FREE**			
1 Presentation box for offers 1, 2 and 3		£5.00	£20.00		

TOTAL 1

JOHANSENS PRINTED GUIDES 2000

CODE	TITLE	PRICE	QTY	TOTAL
A	Recommended Hotels – Great Britain & Ireland 2000	£19.95		
B	Recommended Country Houses & Small Hotels – Great Britain & Ireland 2000	£11.95		
C	Recommended Traditional Inns, Hotels & Restaurants – Great Britain 2000	£10.95		
NEW D	Recommended Holiday Cottages – Great Britain & Ireland 2000	£4.99		
E	Historic Houses, Castles & Gardens 2000	£4.99		
F	Museums & Galleries 2000	£8.95		
G	Recommended Hotels – Europe & The Mediterranean 2000	£15.95		
NEW H	Recommended Hotels – Europe & The Mediterranean 2000 (French Language)	£15.95		
NEW J	Recommended Hotels – Europe & The Mediterranean 2000 (German Language)	£15.95		
K	Recommended Hotels & Inns – North America, Bermuda & The Caribbean 2000	£12.95		
NEW L	Recommended Hotels & Game Lodges – Southern Africa, Mauritius & The Seychelles 2000	£9.95		
M	Recommended Business Meeting Venues 2000	£20.00		

JOHANSENS CD ROMs DIGITAL COLLECTION 2000

CODE	TITLE	PRICE	QTY	TOTAL
N	The Guide 2000 – Great Britain & Ireland	£29.95		
O	The Guide 2000 – Europe & The Mediterranean (English, French, German Language)	£22.95		
P	The Guide 2000 – North America, Bermuda & The Caribbean	£16.95		
NEW Q	The Guide 2000 – Southern Africa, Mauritius & The Seychelles	£16.95		
R	Business Meeting Venues 2000	£20.00		
S	Privilege Card 2000 (Free with your order. Additional Cards £20 each)	£20.00		

Postage & Packing (UK) £4.50 or £2.50 for single order and CD-ROMs

Outside UK add £5 or £3 for single orders and CD-ROMs

TOTAL 2

GRAND TOTAL 1+2+P&P

Name	(Mr/Mrs/Miss)	
Address		
		Postcode
Card No.		Exp Date
Signature		

I have chosen my Johansens Guides/CD-ROMs and

☐ I enclose a cheque for £ _____ payable to Johansens

☐ I enclose my order on company letterheading, please invoice (UK only)

☐ Please debit my credit/charge card account (please tick).

☐ MasterCard ☐ Diners ☐ Amex

☐ Visa ☐ Switch (Issue Number) _____

A23

GUEST SURVEY REPORT
JOHANSENS RECOMMENDED HOLIDAY COTTAGES

**Your own Johansens 'inspection' gives reliability to our guides
and assists in the selection of Award Nominations**

Name of Property: _____

Location: _____

Page No: _____

Date of visit: _____

Name of guest _____

Address: _____

_____ Postcode _____

Please tick one box in each category below:	Excellent	Good	Disappointing	Poor
Accommodation				
Indoor Facilities				
Outdoor Facilities				
Welcome/Friendliness				
Value For Money				

Occasionally we may allow other reputable organisations to write with offers which may be of interest.
If you prefer not to hear from them, tick this box ☐

To: Johansens, FREEPOST (CB264), 43 Millharbour, London E14 9BR

ORDER FORM

Call our 24hr credit card hotline FREEPHONE 0800 269 397.

Simply indicate which title(s) you require by putting the quantity in the boxes provided. Choose your preferred method of payment and mail to Johansens, FREEPOST (CB 264), 43 Millharbour, London E14 9BR, England (no stamp needed). Your FREE gifts will automatically be dispatched with your order. Fax orders welcome on 0171 537 3594

CHOOSE FROM 7 SPECIAL GUIDE COLLECTIONS – SAVE UP TO £56

TITLE	Normal Price	PRICE	SAVE	QTY	TOTAL
OFFER ONE – The Basic Collection					
3 Johansens Guides A+B+C	£42.85	£36.00	£6.85		
OFFER TWO – The Extended Collection					
4 Johansens Guides A+B+C+G	£58.80	£46.00	£12.80		
OFFER THREE – The Full Selection					
5 Johansens Guides A+B+C+G+K PLUS Southern Africa Guide **FREE**	£71.75	£56.00	£15.75		
OFFER FOUR - The Executive Collection					
Business Meeting Venues Guide & CD-ROM M+R	£40.00	£30.00	£10.00		
OFFER FIVE - The Holiday Pack					
3 Johansens Guides D+E+F	£18.93	£9.99	£8.94		
OFFER SIX - The Digital Collection					
3 Johansens CD-ROMs N+O+P PLUS Southern Africa CD-ROM Q **FREE**	£69.85	£59.85	£10.00		
OFFER SEVEN - The Chairman's Collection					
Business Meeting Venues Guide & CD-ROMs M+R **PLUS** 5 Johansens Boxed Guides A+B+C+G+K, **PLUS** D+E+F, **PLUS** 3 CD-ROMs N+O+P **PLUS** Southern Africa Guide/CD ROM Q **FREE**, **PLUS** Mystery Gift **FREE**	£205.53	£149.00	£56.53		
Privilege Card	£20.00	**FREE**			
1 Presentation box for offers 1, 2 and 3		£5.00	£20.00		

TOTAL 1

JOHANSENS PRINTED GUIDES 2000

CODE	TITLE	PRICE	QTY	TOTAL
A	Recommended Hotels – Great Britain & Ireland 2000	£19.95		
B	Recommended Country Houses & Small Hotels – Great Britain & Ireland 2000	£11.95		
C	Recommended Traditional Inns, Hotels & Restaurants – Great Britain 2000	£10.95		
NEW D	Recommended Holiday Cottages – Great Britain & Ireland 2000	£4.99		
E	Historic Houses, Castles & Gardens 2000	£4.99		
F	Museums & Galleries 2000	£8.95		
G	Recommended Hotels – Europe & The Mediterranean 2000	£15.95		
NEW H	Recommended Hotels – Europe & The Mediterranean 2000 (French Language)	£15.95		
NEW J	Recommended Hotels – Europe & The Mediterranean 2000 (German Language)	£15.95		
K	Recommended Hotels & Inns – North America, Bermuda & The Caribbean 2000	£12.95		
NEW L	Recommended Hotels & Game Lodges – Southern Africa, Mauritius & The Seychelles 2000	£9.95		
M	Recommended Business Meeting Venues 2000	£20.00		

JOHANSENS CD ROMs DIGITAL COLLECTION 2000

CODE	TITLE	PRICE	QTY	TOTAL
N	The Guide 2000 – Great Britain & Ireland	£29.95		
O	The Guide 2000 – Europe & The Mediterranean (English, French, German Language)	£22.95		
P	The Guide 2000 – North America, Bermuda & The Caribbean	£16.95		
NEW Q	The Guide 2000 – Southern Africa, Mauritius & The Seychelles	£16.95		
R	Business Meeting Venues 2000	£20.00		
S	Privilege Card 2000 (Free with your order. Additional Cards £20 each)	£20.00		

Postage & Packing (UK) £4.50 or £2.50 for single order and CD-ROMs

Outside UK add £5 or £3 for single orders and CD-ROMs

TOTAL 2

GRAND TOTAL 1+2+P&P

Name	(Mr/Mrs/Miss)
Address	
	Postcode
Card No.	Exp Date
Signature	

I have chosen my Johansens Guides/CD-ROMs and

☐ I enclose a cheque for £ _____ payable to Johansens

☐ I enclose my order on company letterheading, please invoice (UK only)

☐ Please debit my credit/charge card account (please tick).

☐ MasterCard ☐ Diners ☐ Amex

☐ Visa ☐ Switch (Issue Number) _____

A23

GUEST SURVEY REPORT
JOHANSENS RECOMMENDED HOLIDAY COTTAGES

Your own Johansens 'inspection' gives reliability to our guides and assists in the selection of Award Nominations

Name of Property: _____

Location: _____

Page No: _____

Date of visit: _____

Name of guest _____

Address: _____

_____Postcode _____

Please tick one box in each category below:	*Excellent*	*Good*	*Disappointing*	*Poor*
Accommodation				
Indoor Facilities				
Outdoor Facilities				
Welcome/Friendliness				
Value For Money				

Occasionally we may allow other reputable organisations to write with offers which may be of interest. If you prefer not to hear from them, tick this box ☐

To: Johansens, FREEPOST (CB264), 43 Millharbour, London E14 9BR

ORDER FORM

Call our 24hr credit card hotline FREEPHONE 0800 269 397.

Simply indicate which title(s) you require by putting the quantity in the boxes provided. Choose your preferred method of payment and mail to Johansens, FREEPOST (CB 264), 43 Millharbour, London E14 9BR, England (no stamp needed). Your FREE gifts will automatically be dispatched with your order. Fax orders welcome on 0171 537 3594

CHOOSE FROM 7 SPECIAL GUIDE COLLECTIONS – SAVE UP TO £56

TITLE	Normal Price	PRICE	SAVE	QTY	TOTAL
OFFER ONE – The Basic Collection					
3 Johansens Guides A+B+C	£42.85	£36.00	£6.85		
OFFER TWO – The Extended Collection					
4 Johansens Guides A+B+C+G	£58.80	£46.00	£12.80		
OFFER THREE – The Full Selection					
5 Johansens Guides A+B+C+G+K PLUS Southern Africa Guide **FREE**	£71.75	£56.00	£15.75		
OFFER FOUR - The Executive Collection					
Business Meeting Venues Guide & CD-ROM M+R	£40.00	£30.00	£10.00		
OFFER FIVE - The Holiday Pack					
3 Johansens Guides D+E+F	£18.93	£9.99	£8.94		
OFFER SIX - The Digital Collection					
3 Johansens CD-ROMs N+O+P PLUS Southern Africa CD-ROM Q **FREE**	£69.85	£59.85	£10.00		
OFFER SEVEN - The Chairman's Collection					
Business Meeting Venues Guide & CD-ROMs M+R **PLUS** 5 Johansens Boxed Guides A+B+C+G+K, **PLUS** D+E+F, **PLUS** 3 CD-ROMs N+O+P **PLUS** Southern Africa Guide/CD ROM Q **FREE**, **PLUS** Mystery Gift **FREE**	£205.53	£149.00	£56.53		
Privilege Card	£20.00	**FREE**			
1 Presentation box for offers 1, 2 and 3		£5.00	£20.00		

TOTAL 1

JOHANSENS PRINTED GUIDES 2000

CODE	TITLE	PRICE	QTY	TOTAL
A	Recommended Hotels – Great Britain & Ireland 2000	£19.95		
B	Recommended Country Houses & Small Hotels – Great Britain & Ireland 2000	£11.95		
C	Recommended Traditional Inns, Hotels & Restaurants – Great Britain 2000	£10.95		
NEW D	Recommended Holiday Cottages – Great Britain & Ireland 2000	£4.99		
E	Historic Houses, Castles & Gardens 2000	£4.99		
F	Museums & Galleries 2000	£8.95		
G	Recommended Hotels – Europe & The Mediterranean 2000	£15.95		
NEW H	Recommended Hotels – Europe & The Mediterranean 2000 (French Language)	£15.95		
NEW J	Recommended Hotels – Europe & The Mediterranean 2000 (German Language)	£15.95		
K	Recommended Hotels & Inns – North America, Bermuda & The Caribbean 2000	£12.95		
NEW L	Recommended Hotels & Game Lodges – Southern Africa, Mauritius & The Seychelles 2000	£9.95		
M	Recommended Business Meeting Venues 2000	£20.00		

JOHANSENS CD ROMs DIGITAL COLLECTION 2000

CODE	TITLE	PRICE	QTY	TOTAL
N	The Guide 2000 – Great Britain & Ireland	£29.95		
O	The Guide 2000 – Europe & The Mediterranean (English, French, German Language)	£22.95		
P	The Guide 2000 – North America, Bermuda & The Caribbean	£16.95		
NEW Q	The Guide 2000 – Southern Africa, Mauritius & The Seychelles	£16.95		
R	Business Meeting Venues 2000	£20.00		
S	Privilege Card 2000 (Free with your order. Additional Cards £20 each)	£20.00		

Postage & Packing (UK) £4.50 or £2.50 for single order and CD-ROMs
Outside UK add £5 or £3 for single orders and CD-ROMs

TOTAL 2

GRAND TOTAL 1+2+P&P

Name (Mr/Mrs/Miss)

Address

Postcode

Card No.

Exp Date

Signature

I have chosen my Johansens Guides/CD-ROMs and

☐ I enclose a cheque for £ _____ payable to Johansens

☐ I enclose my order on company letterheading, please invoice (UK only)

☐ Please debit my credit/charge card account (please tick).

☐ MasterCard ☐ Diners ☐ Amex

☐ Visa ☐ Switch (Issue Number)

A23

GUEST SURVEY REPORT
JOHANSENS RECOMMENDED HOLIDAY COTTAGES

**Your own Johansens 'inspection' gives reliability to our guides
and assists in the selection of Award Nominations**

Name of Property: _____

Location: _____

Page No: _____

Date of visit: _____

Name of guest _____

Address: _____

_____ Postcode _____

Please tick one box in each category below:	Excellent	Good	Disappointing	Poor
Accommodation				
Indoor Facilities				
Outdoor Facilities				
Welcome/Friendliness				
Value For Money				

Occasionally we may allow other reputable organisations to write with offers which may be of interest.
If you prefer not to hear from them, tick this box ☐

To: Johansens, FREEPOST (CB264), 43 Millharbour, London E14 9BR

ORDER FORM

Call our 24hr credit card hotline FREEPHONE 0800 269 397.

Simply indicate which title(s) you require by putting the quantity in the boxes provided. Choose your preferred method of payment and mail to Johansens, FREEPOST (CB 264), 43 Millharbour, London E14 9BR, England (no stamp needed). Your FREE gifts will automatically be dispatched with your order. Fax orders welcome on 0171 537 3594

CHOOSE FROM 7 SPECIAL GUIDE COLLECTIONS – SAVE UP TO £56

TITLE	Normal Price	PRICE	SAVE	QTY	TOTAL
OFFER ONE – The Basic Collection					
3 Johansens Guides A+B+C	£42.85	£36.00	£6.85		
OFFER TWO – The Extended Collection					
4 Johansens Guides A+B+C+G	£58.80	£46.00	£12.80		
OFFER THREE – The Full Selection					
5 Johansens Guides A+B+C+G+K PLUS Southern Africa Guide **FREE**	£71.75	£56.00	£15.75		
OFFER FOUR - The Executive Collection					
Business Meeting Venues Guide & CD-ROM M+R	£40.00	£30.00	£10.00		
OFFER FIVE - The Holiday Pack					
3 Johansens Guides D+E+F	£18.93	£9.99	£8.94		
OFFER SIX - The Digital Collection					
3 Johansens CD-ROMs N+O+P PLUS Southern Africa CD-ROM Q **FREE**	£69.85	£59.85	£10.00		
OFFER SEVEN - The Chairman's Collection					
Business Meeting Venues Guide & CD-ROMs M+R **PLUS** 5 Johansens Boxed Guides A+B+C+G+K, **PLUS** D+E+F, **PLUS** 3 CD-ROMs N+O+P **PLUS** Southern Africa Guide/CD ROM Q **FREE**, **PLUS** Mystery Gift **FREE**	£205.53	£149.00	£56.53		
Privilege Card	£20.00	**FREE**			
1 Presentation box for offers 1, 2 and 3		£5.00	£20.00		

TOTAL 1

JOHANSENS PRINTED GUIDES 2000

	CODE	TITLE	PRICE	QTY	TOTAL
	A	Recommended Hotels – Great Britain & Ireland 2000	£19.95		
	B	Recommended Country Houses & Small Hotels – Great Britain & Ireland 2000	£11.95		
	C	Recommended Traditional Inns, Hotels & Restaurants – Great Britain 2000	£10.95		
NEW	D	Recommended Holiday Cottages – Great Britain & Ireland 2000	£4.99		
	E	Historic Houses, Castles & Gardens 2000	£4.99		
	F	Museums & Galleries 2000	£8.95		
	G	Recommended Hotels – Europe & The Mediterranean 2000	£15.95		
NEW	H	Recommended Hotels – Europe & The Mediterranean 2000 (French Language)	£15.95		
NEW	J	Recommended Hotels – Europe & The Mediterranean 2000 (German Language)	£15.95		
	K	Recommended Hotels & Inns – North America, Bermuda & The Caribbean 2000	£12.95		
NEW	L	Recommended Hotels & Game Lodges – Southern Africa, Mauritius & The Seychelles 2000	£9.95		
	M	Recommended Business Meeting Venues 2000	£20.00		

JOHANSENS CD ROMs DIGITAL COLLECTION 2000

	CODE	TITLE	PRICE	QTY	TOTAL
	N	The Guide 2000 – Great Britain & Ireland	£29.95		
	O	The Guide 2000 – Europe & The Mediterranean (English, French, German Language)	£22.95		
	P	The Guide 2000 – North America, Bermuda & The Caribbean	£16.95		
NEW	Q	The Guide 2000 – Southern Africa, Mauritius & The Seychelles	£16.95		
	R	Business Meeting Venues 2000	£20.00		
	S	Privilege Card 2000 (Free with your order. Additional Cards £20 each)	£20.00		

Postage & Packing (UK) £4.50 or £2.50 for single order and CD-ROMs
Outside UK add £5 or £3 for single orders and CD-ROMs

TOTAL 2

GRAND TOTAL 1+2+P&P

Name (Mr/Mrs/Miss)

Address

Postcode

Card No.

Exp Date

Signature

I have chosen my Johansens Guides/CD-ROMs and

☐ I enclose a cheque for £ _____ payable to Johansens

☐ I enclose my order on company letterheading, please invoice (UK only)

☐ Please debit my credit/charge card account (please tick).

☐ MasterCard ☐ Diners ☐ Amex

☐ Visa ☐ Switch (Issue Number) _____

A23

GUEST SURVEY REPORT
JOHANSENS RECOMMENDED HOLIDAY COTTAGES

**Your own Johansens 'inspection' gives reliability to our guides
and assists in the selection of Award Nominations**

Name of Property: _____   _____

Location: _____   W0006608   _____

Page No:_____

Date of visit: _____

Name of guest _____

Address: _____

_____Postcode _____

Please tick one box in each category below:	Excellent	Good	Disappointing	Poor
Accommodation				
Indoor Facilities				
Outdoor Facilities				
Welcome/Friendliness				
Value For Money				

Occasionally we may allow other reputable organisations to write with offers which may be of interest.
If you prefer not to hear from them, tick this box ☐

To: Johansens, FREEPOST (CB264), 43 Millharbour, London E14 9BR